Revise GCSE

Additional Science

Ian Honeysett, John Sadler and Carol Tear

Contents

This book and your GCSE course

	AQA A	AQA B	EDEXCEL 360
Web address	www.aqa.org.uk		www.edexcel.org.uk
Specification number	4463		none
Modular tests	none		Schools have to choose two out of three
Terminal papers	3 papers: one in biology, one in chemistry and one in physics 25% each		Multiple choice tests (3) 30% 3 structured exams Jan/June 30% Centre-devised portfolios 30%
Availability of exams	Jan, June		Nov, March, June
Coursework	25%		90%
BIOLOGY			
Cells and growth	B2.11.2, B2.11.3, B1.11.6, B2.11.8		B2.1, B2.2, B2.3
Ecology	B2.11.4 B2.11.3 B2.11.5		B2.3
Further physiology	B2.11.7 B2.11.6		
Genes and biotechnology	B2.11.8 B2.11.6		B2.1-2
CHEMISTRY			
Atoms, bonding and structure	C2.12.1, C2.12.3		C2.6, C2.7
The periodic table	C15.4, C2.12.1, C2.12.6, C2.11.5		C1a5, C2.5, C2.6, C3.3, B2.3
Calculations in chemistry	C2.12.3, C2.12.5, C2.12.6		C2.6, C2.5, C2.8
Acids, bases, salts and eletrolysis	C2.12.6, C2.11.2		C1a, C2.6, C2.5
PHYSICS			
Forces and motion	P2.13.3, P2.13.1, P2.13.4, P2.13.2		P2.9, P2.10
Electricity	P2.13.8, P2.13.7, P2.13.5, P2.13.6		P2.12
Waves and radiation			P2.11
Nuclear physics	P2.13.9		P2.11, P2.12

Visit your awarding body for full details of your course or download your complete GCSE specificatio

Use these pages to get to know your course
- Make sure you know your exam board
- Check which specification you are doing

- Know how your course is assessed:
  - what format are the papers?
  - how is coursework assessed?
  - how many papers?

OCR A	OCR B	
www.ocr.org.uk		
J631	J641	
Units 1-3 each 40 min, 40 marks, 16.7%	2 x 60 min	
Unit 4 Ideas in context, 45 min, 16.7%	none	
Jan, June	Jan, June	
33.3%	33.3%	
B5.1, B4.2, B5.2, B5.3	B3a, B3d, B4a, B3b, B3e, B3	
	B4d, B4e, B4f, B4g, B4h	
B4.1, B4.4, B6.1–6	B2e, B3c, B3a, B3g	
	B3a, B3g	
C4.2, C5.1, C5.2, C5.4	C3a, C3b, C3h, C3f	
C4.1, C5.1, C5.3	C3c, C3d, C3e, C4h,	
C6.1, C6.2	C4b, C4d, C4f, C4c	
C6.1, C5.4, C6.2	C4a, C3f, C2d, C5d	
P4.1.1, P4.1, P4.2, P4.3, P4.4	P3a, P3b, P3h, P3c, P3e, P3f, P3g, P5d	
P5.1. P5.2, P3.4, P5.3, P5.5, P5.4	P4a, P4b, P4c	
	P4d, P4e	
P6.1, P6.3, P6.2, P6.4	P4g, P4e, P4f, P4h	

Preparing for the examination

Planning your study

The last few months before taking your final GCSE examinations are very important in achieving your best grade. However, the success can be assisted by an organised approach throughout the course. This is particularly important now as all the science courses are available in units.

- After completing a topic in school or college, go through the topic again in your Revise GCSE Science Study Guide. Copy out the main points on a sheet of paper or use a highlighter pen to emphasise them.
- Much of memory is visual. Make sure your notes are laid out attractively using spaces and symbols. If they are easy to read and attractive to the eye, they will be easier to remember.
- A couple of days later, try to write out these key points from memory. Check differences between what you wrote originally and what you wrote later.
- If you have written your notes on a piece of paper, keep this for revision later.
- Try some questions in the book and check your answers.
- Decide whether you have fully mastered the topic and write down any weaknesses you think you have.

Preparing a revision programme

Before an external examination, look at the list of topics in your examination board's specification. Go through and identify which topics you feel you need to concentrate on. It is a temptation at this time to spend valuable revision time on the things you already know and can do. It makes you feel good but does not move you forward.

When you feel you have mastered all the topics, spend time trying sample questions that can be found on your examination board's website. Each time, check your answers with the answers given. In the final week, go back to your summary sheets (or highlighting in the book).

How this book will help you

Revise GCSE Science Study Guide will help you because:

- it contains the essential content for your GCSE course without the extra material that will not be examined
- it contains GCSE Exam Practice Questions to help you to confirm your understanding
- examination questions from 2007 are different from those in the past. Trying past questions will not help you when answering some parts of the questions in 2007. The questions in this book have been written by experienced examiners.
- the summary table will give you a quick reference to the requirements for your examination

Four ways to improve your grade

1. Read the question carefully

Many students fail to answer the actual question set. Perhaps they misread the question or answer a similar question they have seen before. Read the question once right through and then again more slowly. Some students underline or highlight key words in the question as they read it through. Questions at GCSE contain a lot of information. You should be concerned if you are not using the information in your answer.

2. Give enough detail

If a part of a question is worth three marks you should make at least three separate points. Be careful that you do not make the same point three times. Draw diagrams with a ruler and label with straight lines.

3. Correct use of scientific language

There is important scientific vocabulary you should use. Try to use the correct scientific terms in your answers. The way scientific language is used is often a difference between successful and unsuccessful students. As you revise, make a list of scientific terms you meet and check that you understand the meaning of these words. Learn all the definitions. These are easy marks and they reward effort and good preparation.

4. Show your working

All science papers include calculations. Learn a set method for solving a calculation and use that method. You should always show your working in full. Then, if you make an arithmetical mistake, you may still receive marks for correct science. Check that your answer is given to the correct number of significant figures and give the correct units.

How Science Works

From 2007, all GCSE science courses must cover certain factual detail, similar to the detail that has been required for many years. Now, however, each course must also include study of 'How Science Works'.

This includes four main areas:

- **Data, evidence, theories and explanations**
  This involves learning about how scientists work, the differences between data and theories and how scientists form theories.

- **Practical skills**
  How to test a scientific idea including collecting the data and deciding how reliable and valid it is.

- **Communication skills**
  Learn how to present information in graphs and tables and to be able to analyse information that has been provided in different forms.

- **Applications and implications of science**
  Learning about how new scientific discoveries become accepted and some of the benefits, drawbacks and risks of new developments.

The different examining bodies have included material about how science works in different parts of their examinations. Often it is in the coursework but you are also likely to come across some questions in your written papers. Do not panic about this and think that you have not learnt this work. Remember these questions test your skills and not your memory; that is why the situations are likely to be unfamiliar. The examiners want you to show what you know, understand and can do.

To help you with this, there are sections at the end of each chapter called How Science Works and questions about how science works in the Exam Practice Questions. This should give you an idea of what to expect.

Chapter

1 Cells and growth

The following topics are covered in this chapter:

- Cell structure and function
- Transport in cells
- Growth and asexual reproduction
- Cellular processes

1.1 Cell structure and function

Animal and plant cells

Plant and animal cells have a number of structures in common.

They all have:
- a **nucleus** that carries genetic information and controls the cell
- a **cell membrane** which controls the movement of substances in and out of the cell
- **cytoplasm** where most of the chemical reactions happen.

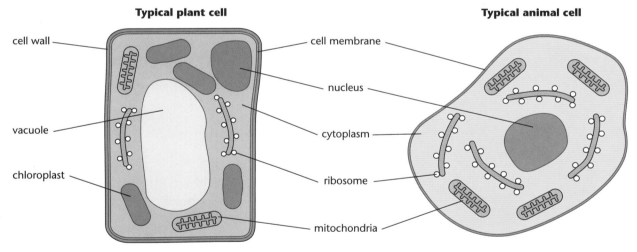

Fig. 1.1 Animal and plant cells

There are four main differences between plant and animal cells:
- plant cells have a strong **cell wall** made of cellulose, animal cells do not
- plant cells have a large permanent **vacuole** containing cell sap, vacuoles in animal cells are small and temporary
- plant cells may have **chloroplasts** containing chlorophyll for photosynthesis. Animal cells never contain chloroplasts.

Plant and animal cells also have many smaller structures in the cytoplasm. These can be seen by using an electron microscope.

Mitochondria are the site of respiration in the cell and **ribosomes** are where proteins are made.

Enzymes

KEY POINT Enzymes are biological catalysts. They are produced in all living organisms and control all the chemical reactions that occur.

Most of the chemical reactions that occur in living organisms would happen too slowly without enzymes. Increased temperatures would speed up the reactions, but using enzymes means that the reactions are fast enough at 37 °C. These reactions include photosynthesis, respiration and protein synthesis.

Enzymes are protein molecules. They are made of a long chain of amino acids that is folded up to make a particular shape. They have a slot or a groove, called the **active site**, into which the substrate fits. The reaction then takes place and the products leave the enzyme.

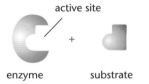

active site

enzyme + substrate → enzyme–substrate complex → ready to be used again + 2 products have been produced

Fig. 1.2 The Lock and Key theory of enzymes.

KEY POINT This explanation for how enzymes work is called the Lock and Key theory.

This theory explains why an enzyme will only work on one type of substrate. They are described as **specific**.

Enzymes work best at a particular temperature and pH. This is called the **optimum** temperature or pH.

If the temperature is too low then the substrate and the enzyme molecules will not collide so often and the reaction will slow down.

If the shape of the enzyme molecule changes then the substrate will not easily fit into the active site. This means that the reaction will slow down.

Various factors may cause this to happen:
● high temperatures
● extremes of pH.

If the shape of the enzyme molecule is irreversibly changed then it is described as being **denatured**.

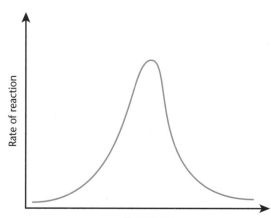

Fig. 1.3 Rate of reaction of an enzyme.

DNA and protein synthesis

OCR A   B5.2
OCR B   B3a
AQA   B11.8
EDEXCEL 360 B2.1

The nucleus controls the chemical reactions occurring in the cell. This is because it contains the genetic material. This is contained in structures called **chromosomes** which are made of a chemical called **DNA**.

DNA is a large molecule with a very important structure:

- it has two strands
- the strands are twisted to make a shape called a double helix
- each strand is a long chain of molecules called bases
- there are only four bases called A, T, G and C
- links between the bases hold the two chains together.

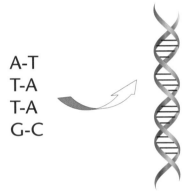

Fig. 1.4 The structure of DNA.

DNA controls the cell by carrying the code for proteins. Each different protein is made of a particular order of amino acids, so DNA must code for this order.

> **KEY POINT** A gene is a length of DNA that codes for the order of amino acids in one protein.

Scientists now know that each amino acid in a protein is coded for by each set of three bases along the DNA molecule.

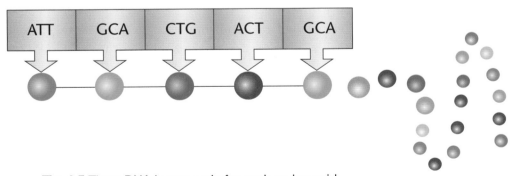

Fig. 1.5 Three DNA bases code for each amino acid.

The problem is that proteins are made on ribosomes in the cytoplasm and DNA is kept in the nucleus. The cell has to use a messenger molecule to copy the message from DNA and to carry the code to the ribosomes. This molecule is called **RNA**.

1.2 Growth and asexual reproduction

Cell division

 OCR A   B5.1
OCR B   B3a

Before a cell divides, two things must happen. First new cell structures such as mitochondria must be made. Then the DNA must copy itself. The structure of DNA allows this to happen in a rather neat way.

- The double helix of DNA unwinds and the two strands come apart or 'unzip'.
- The bases on each strand attract their complementary bases and so two new molecules are made.

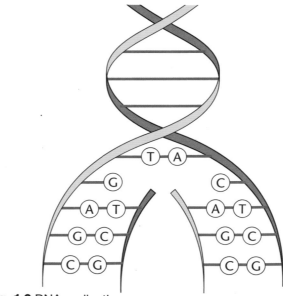

Fig. 1.6 DNA replication.

Mitosis and meiosis

 OCR A   B5.1
OCR B   B3a
AQA   B2.11.8
EDEXCEL 360   B2.2

Cells divide for a number of reasons. There are two types of cell division and they are used for different reasons.

KEY POINT   **There are two types of cell division, meiosis and mitosis.**

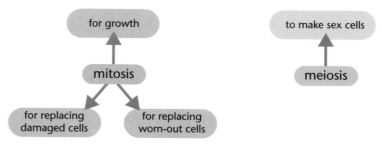

Fig. 1.7 Uses of mitosis and meiosis.

In **mitosis**, two cells are produced from one. As long as the chromosomes have been copied exactly, then each new daughter cell will have the same number of chromosomes and the same information as each other and the original cell.

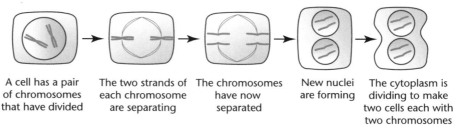

A cell has a pair of chromosomes that have divided   The two strands of each chromosome are separating   The chromosomes have now separated   New nuclei are forming   The cytoplasm is dividing to make two cells each with two chromosomes

Fig. 1.8 Mitosis.

In **meiosis**, the chromosomes are also copied once but the cell divides twice. This makes four cells each with half the number of chromosomes, one from each pair.

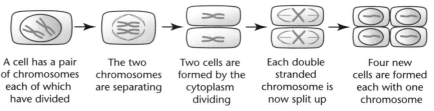

A cell has a pair of chromosomes each of which have divided   The two chromosomes are separating   Two cells are formed by the cytoplasm dividing   Each double stranded chromosome is now split up   Four new cells are formed each with one chromosome

Fig. 1.9 Meiosis.

> **KEY POINT**
>
> Cells with one chromosome from each pair are called haploid and can be used as gametes. When two gametes join, the diploid or full number of chromosomes is produced.

Growth and development

OCR A   B5.3
OCR B   B3d, 3e
AQA   B2.11.8
EDEXCEL 360   B2.2

Most organisms are multi-cellular. This means that they are made up of a large number of cells. This has a number of advantages:

● it allows organisms to be larger
● it allows the cells to become specialised for different jobs.

When gametes join at fertilisation, this produces a single cell called a **zygote**. This soon starts to divide many times by mitosis to produce many identical cells.

These cells then start to become specialised for different jobs.

> **KEY POINT**
>
> The production of different types of cells for different jobs is called differentiation.

These differentiated cells can then form tissues and organs. Once a cell has differentiated, it cannot form other types of cells. Although it has the same genes as all the other cells, many are turned off so it only makes the proteins it needs.

Embryonic stem cells can produce a greater range of different cells than adult stem cells.

Some cells in the embryo and in the adult keep the ability to form other types of cells. They are called **stem cells**. Scientists are now trying to use stem cells to replace cells that have stopped working or been damaged. This may have the potential to cure a number of diseases.

Cells and growth

Human growth and development

OCR B **B3e**

Humans grow at different rates at different times of their lives.

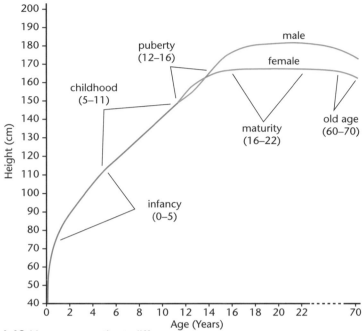

Fig. 1.10 Human growth at different ages.

The various parts of their body also grow at different rates at different times.

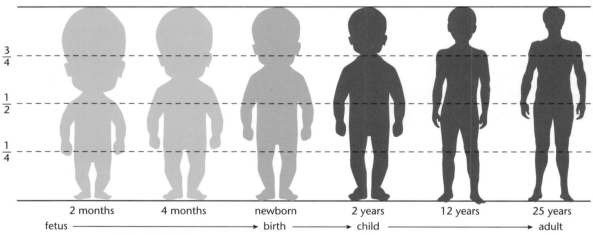

Fig. 1.11 Relative sizes of different parts of the body.

Plant growth and development

OCR A **B5.3**
OCR B **B3d, 3e**
AQA **B2.11.8**
Edexcel 360 **B2.2**

Like animals, plants grow by making new cells through mitosis. The cells then differentiate into tissues like xylem and phloem. These tissues then form organs such as roots, leaves and flowers.

Growth in plants is different from animal growth in a number of ways:

- Plant cells enlarge much more than animal cells after they are produced. This increases the size of the plant.
- Cells tend to divide at the ends of roots and shoots. This means that plants grow from their tips.

Plant cells that can produce new types of cells are called meristematic.

- Animals usually stop growing when they reach a certain size, but plants carry on growing.
- Many plant cells keep the ability to produce new types of cells. In animals only stem cells can do this.

Growth in plants is controlled by chemicals called **plant growth substances** or **plant hormones**. They control:

- the rate and direction that roots and shoots grow
- the time that plants flower
- the ripening of fruits.

> **KEY POINT**   The main type of plant hormones are called auxins.

By controlling the growth of plants, auxins can allow plants to respond to changes happening around them. This means that the roots and shoots of plants can respond to gravity or light in different ways.

change	Type of growth	
	shoots	**roots**
gravity	away = negatively geotropic	towards = positively geotropic
light	towards = positively phototropic	away = negatively phototropic

Auxins change the direction that roots and shoots grow by changing the rate that the cells elongate.

Growing towards the light means that shoots can gather more light for photosynthesis.

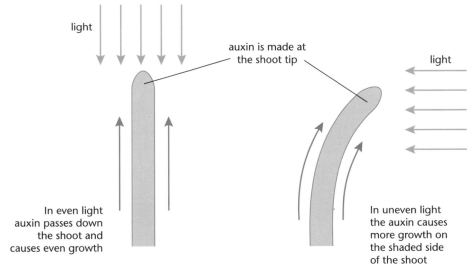

Fig. 1.12 How auxins control tropisms.

Gardeners can use auxins to help them control the growth of their plants.

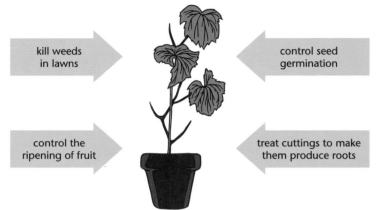

kill weeds in lawns	control seed germination
control the ripening of fruit	treat cuttings to make them produce roots

Fig. 1.13 Uses of auxins.

Cloning

OCR A	B5.3
OCR B	B3h
AQA	B2.11.8
EDEXCEL 360	B2.2

KEY POINT   **A clone is an identical genetic copy.**

Because plants have many cells that have not yet differentiated, it is easy to produce identical copies of useful plants. Plants may also produce identical copies naturally. This is called asexual reproduction.

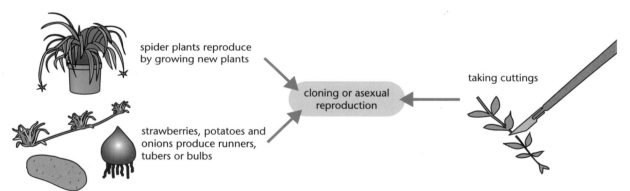

spider plants reproduce by growing new plants

cloning or asexual reproduction

taking cuttings

strawberries, potatoes and onions produce runners, tubers or bulbs

Fig. 1.14 Different types of asexual reproduction.

Producing plants by cloning has a number of advantages and disadvantages.

Advantages	Disadvantages
you know what you are going to get because all the plants will be genetically identical to each other and the parent	the population of plants will be genetically very similar – there will be little variety
you can produce many plants that do not flower very often or are difficult to grow from seeds	because the plants all have the same genes, a disease or change in the environment could kill them all

Cloning animals is much harder to do. Two main methods are used.

- **Cloning embryos.** Embryos are split up at an early stage and the cells are put into host mothers to grow.

- **Cloning adult cells.** The first mammal to be cloned from adult cells was Dolly the sheep.

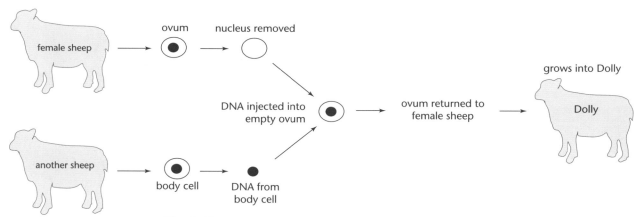

Fig. 1.15 How Dolly was cloned.

Would a cloned person be identical to the donor? Remember how we are brought up is important, not just our genes.

Since Dolly was born, other animals have been cloned and there has been much interest about cloning.

Animals could be cloned for a number of reasons:
● To produce large numbers of animals that produce a good yield of meat or milk.
● To copy animals that have been produced by genetic engineering. They could then be used to produce human protein or organs for human transplants.

If it is possible to produce clones of animals it should also be possible to clone humans.

There could be two possible reasons for cloning humans:
● reproductive cloning to make embryos for infertile couples
● therapeutic cloning to produce embryos that can be used to treat diseases.

The use of embryos to treat disease is possible due to the discovery of stem cells.

It is much easier to find stem cells in an embryo and scientists think that they could be used to repair damaged tissues like injuries to the spinal cord.

There are therefore many different views about cloning:

❝ Both infertility and genetic diseases cause much pain and distress. I think that we should be able to use cloning to treat these problems. ❞

❝ It is not right to clone people because clones are not true individuals and it is not right to destroy embryos to supply stem cells. ❞

1.3 Transport in cells

Transport across the cell membrane

OCR A   B4.2
OCR B   B3b
AQA   B2.11.2

Substances can pass across the cell membrane by three different processes:

- diffusion
- osmosis
- active transport.

> **KEY POINT**
> Diffusion is the movement of a substance from an area of high concentration to an area of low concentration.

Diffusion works because particles are always moving about in a random way.

The rate of diffusion can be increased in a number of ways:

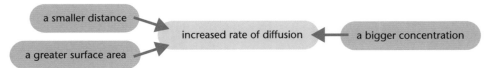

Fig. 1.16 Factors that increase diffusion rate.

Osmosis is really a special type of diffusion. It involves the diffusion of water.

Remember that an area of high water concentration is usually called a dilute solution.

> **KEY POINT**
> Osmosis is the movement of water across a partially permeable membrane from an area of high water concentration to an area of low water concentration.

The cell membrane is an example of a partially permeable membrane. It lets small molecules through, such as water, but stops larger molecules.

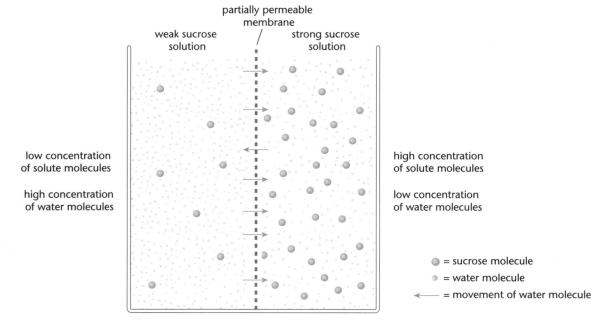

Fig. 1.17 Osmosis.

Turgid cells are very important in helping to support plants. Plants with flaccid cells often wilt.

When plant cells gain water by osmosis, they swell. The cell wall stops them from bursting. This makes the cell stiff or **turgid**. If a plant cell loses water, it goes limp or **flaccid**.

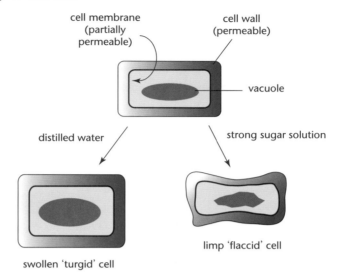

cell membrane (partially permeable)

cell wall (permeable)

vacuole

distilled water

strong sugar solution

swollen 'turgid' cell

limp 'flaccid' cell

Fig. 1.18 Osmosis in plant cells.

Animal cells do not behave in the same way because they do not have a cell wall. They will either swell up and burst or shrink if they gain or lose water.

Sometimes substances have to be moved from a place where they are in low concentration to where they are in high concentration. This is in the opposite direction to diffusion and is called **active transport**.

> **KEY POINT**
>
> Active transport is the movement of a substance against the diffusion gradient with the use of energy from respiration.

Examples of diffusion

 OCR A   B4.2
 OCR B   B3b

There are many examples of the movement of substances by diffusion in plants and animals.

Site	Substances	Direction of movement	Special features
small intestine	digested food materials	from the small intestine into the blood	villi and microvilli give the intestine a large surface area
lungs	gases	oxygen moves from the air to the blood and carbon dioxide moves the opposite way	the alveoli have a large surface area, a moist lining, a good blood supply and a thin wall
placenta	food materials, waste products and gases	oxygen and food moves from the mother to the fetus. Carbon dioxide and waste moves the opposite way	the placenta has a large surface area, a rich blood supply and a thin wall
neurones	transmitter substances	move across synapses	allows nerve impulses to pass from neurone to neurone
leaves	water, carbon dioxide and oxygen	water and oxygen move out of the leaves and carbon dioxide moves in	leaves have a large surface area, pores called stomata and many air spaces

1.4 Cellular processes

Photosynthesis

Plants make their own food by a process called photosynthesis. They take in carbon dioxide and water and turn it into glucose, releasing oxygen as a waste product. The process needs the energy from sunlight and this is trapped by the green pigment chlorophyll.

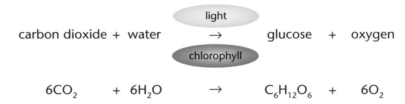

carbon dioxide + water $\xrightarrow[\text{chlorophyll}]{\text{light}}$ glucose + oxygen

$$6CO_2 \quad + \quad 6H_2O \quad \rightarrow \quad C_6H_{12}O_6 \quad + \quad 6O_2$$

Once plants have made glucose, they can convert it into many different things:

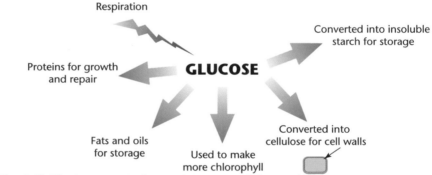

Fig. 1.19 Plants convert glucose into many different things.

Limiting factors

> You can demonstrate most of these effects by counting the bubbles of oxygen given off by pondweed.

The rate of photosynthesis can be increased by providing:
● more light
● more carbon dioxide
● an optimum temperature.

Any of these factors can be limiting factors.

KEY POINT A limiting factor is something that controls how fast a reaction will occur.

Fig. 1.20 Effect of different factors on the rate of photosynthesis.

If more light is provided, it will increase photosynthesis because more energy is available. After a certain point, something else will limit the rate.

More carbon dioxide will again increase the rate up to a point because more raw materials are present. Increasing temperature will make enzymes work faster but high temperatures prevent enzymes from working.

Where does photosynthesis occur?

OCR B   B4a

Photosynthesis occurs mainly in the leaves of a plant.

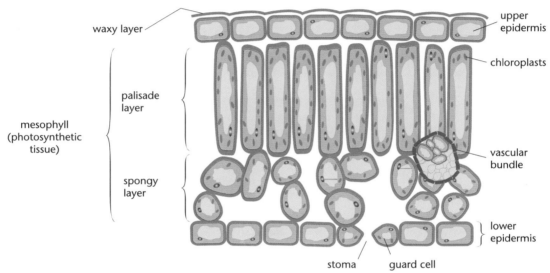

Labels: waxy layer, palisade layer, mesophyll (photosynthetic tissue), spongy layer, upper epidermis, chloroplasts, vascular bundle, lower epidermis, stoma, guard cell

Fig. 1.21 Cross section of a leaf.

The leaves are specially adapted for photosynthesis in a number of ways.

Adaptation	How it helps photosynthesis
a broad shape	provides a large surface area to absorb light and CO_2
a flat shape	the gases do not have too far to diffuse
contains a network of veins	supplies water from the roots and takes away the products
contains many chloroplasts in the palisade layer near the top	traps the maximum amount of light
pores called stomata and air spaces	allow gases to diffuse into the leaf and reach the cells

Aerobic respiration

AQA   B2.11.6
EDEXCEL 360   B2.1

KEY POINT

Aerobic respiration is when glucose reacts with oxygen to release energy. Carbon dioxide and water are released as waste products.

glucose + oxygen → carbon dioxide + water + **energy**

$$C_6H_{12}O_6 + 6O_2 \rightarrow 6CO_2 + 6H_2O + energy$$

The reactions of aerobic respiration take place in mitochondria.

The energy that is released by respiration can be used for many processes:
- to make large molecules from smaller ones (e.g. proteins from amino acids)
- to contract the muscles
- for mammals and birds to keep a constant temperature
- for active transport.

> It is actually the build up of carbon dioxide that makes us breathe faster.

During exercise, the body needs more energy and so the rate of respiration increases. The breathing rate increases to obtain extra oxygen and remove carbon dioxide from the body. The heart beats faster so that the blood can transport the oxygen and carbon dioxide faster. This is why our pulse rate increases.

Anaerobic respiration

EDEXCEL **B2.1**

> **KEY POINT** When not enough oxygen is available, glucose can be broken down by anaerobic respiration.

This may happen in muscle cells during hard exercise.

In humans: glucose → lactic acid + **energy**.

Being able to respire without oxygen sounds a great idea. However, there are two problems:
- Anaerobic respiration releases less than half the energy of that released by aerobic respiration.
- Anaerobic respiration produces lactic acid. Lactic acid causes muscle fatigue and pain.

The build up of lactic acid is called the 'oxygen debt'. After the exercise is finished, extra oxygen is needed by the liver to remove the lactic acid.

HOW SCIENCE WORKS

OCR A	B5.3
OCR B	B3e
AQA	B2.11.8
EDEXCEL 360	B2.2

Stem cells help dogs with dystrophy

Scientists think that a recent experiment with stem cells using dogs is an important step towards treating people.

The experiment focused on Duchenne muscular dystrophy, a muscle-wasting genetic disorder that occurs in about 1 in every 3,500 boys that are born.

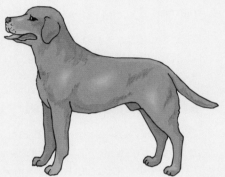

Children with the disorder have trouble walking and nearly all of them lose their ability to walk between ages 7 and 12. They usually die in their 20s because of weakness in their heart and lung muscles. There is no known cure.

The scientists worked with dogs that suffer a type of dystrophy that is very much like the human one. They gave the dogs repeated injections of a kind of stem cell extracted from blood vessels.

Two dogs that were severely disabled by the disease were able to walk faster and even jump after the treatments.

This is just one example of how stem cells may be used to treat people.

One of the main problems is where to get stem cells from.

The most useful stem cells are from early embryos. These cells are called embryonic stem cells and can develop into any other type of cell. If they are taken from a cloned embryo of a person, there is also the big advantage that they will not be rejected by that person. The problem is that extracting the cells involves destroying the embryo.

The search is now on to find other sources of stem cells. There are a number of possibilities.

Setting up a stem cell bank

A company is setting up a new service for parents. The company will take blood from a baby's umbilical cord when it is born. The blood is then frozen and stored.

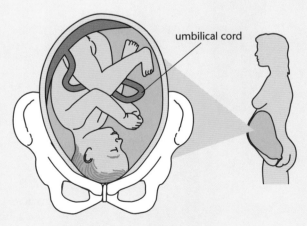

umbilical cord

This is done because the blood contains stem cells. It is stored in the hope it could one day be used to treat certain blood diseases. The cost is £1500.

HOW SCIENCE WORKS

The stem cells found in the umbilical cord are not embryonic stem cells and can only form certain cells in the blood and immune system. The advantage is that they are much easier to obtain than adult stem cells. They are also much less likely to be rejected if given to the person who they were taken from.

They could be used to treat a number of diseases such as leukaemia. The Leukaemia Research charity say that cord blood transplants would offer the best chance of survival to about 40 children each year in Britain.

Stem cells from 'virgin birth'

Some animals, like water fleas, can produce eggs that develop into babies without being fertilised by a male. This is an example of asexual reproduction. This means that all the genetic material comes from the mother. No mammals have been found that can do this.

Scientists have now been able to get a mouse egg to start to divide without being fertilised. The ball of cells cannot produce a mouse because it always dies at an early stage.

Scientists think that they may be able to repeat this with human eggs. This means that they may be able to extract embryonic stem cells from them before they die.

HOW SCIENCE WORKS Questions Here are some people's views about these uses of stem cells. Explain why they might have these views. **[6]**

" *I think that it is wrong to use cloned embryos to extract stem cells.* **"**

" *I am not happy with companies charging to store blood from umbilical cords.* **"**

" *I think that more people would agree to use the ball of cells produced from an unfertilised egg rather than from a cloned embryo.* **"**

Exam practice questions

1.   The following structures are found in plant and animal cells.
     Match words **A**, **B**, **C**, and **D**, with the numbers 1–4 in the sentences.
     A   mitochondria
     B   cell wall
     C   vacuole
     D   cell membrane

     All organisms release energy from food, this largely happens in the ____**1**____. Cells
     take up water by osmosis because the ____**2**____ is selectively permeable. The
     ____**3**____ stores some sugars and salts. Plant cells are limited to how much water
     they can take up because the ____**4**____ resists the uptake of too much water.   **[4]**

2.   Complete the table putting a tick (✓) or a cross (✗) in the blank boxes.

	Osmosis	Diffusion	Active transport
Can cause a substance to enter a cell	.	✓	
Needs energy from respiration	✗		
Can move a substance against a concentration gradient	✗		
Is responsible for oxygen moving into the red blood cells in the lungs	.		✗

[4]

3.   The boxes contain some chemicals that are found in the cell and some functions.
     Draw straight lines to join each chemical to its correct function.

Chemical   **Function**

amino acids   Chromosomes are made from this chemical

bases   This is the chemical messenger that carries
                                  the genetic code out of the nucleus

DNA   The order of these chemicals on the
                                  chromosomes codes for proteins

RNA   These chemicals join together to make
                                  a protein molecule   **[3]**

4.   Complete the table by writing the correct numbers in each box.

The number of chromosomes in a human body cell.	
The number of cells made from one cell when it divides by meiosis.	
The number of chromosomes in a human sperm cell.	
The number of strands in each DNA molecule.	

[4]

Exam practice questions

5. All the cells in the human body have about 20 000 genes.
   Scientists have studied some organs to see how many of these genes are used by cells in each organ.
   This number is shown on the diagram.

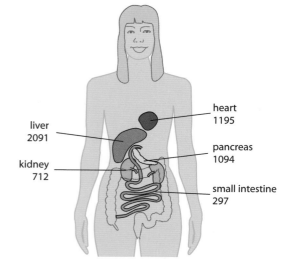

liver
2091

heart
1195

pancreas
1094

kidney
712

small intestine
297

   (a) Write down precisely where in a cell the genes are found. [2]
   (b) Genes code for proteins.
       Explain how each gene can code for a different protein. [2]
   (c) What percentage of its genes does each pancreas cell actually use? [1]
   (d) Which organ on the diagram would you expect to carry out the most chemical reactions?
       Explain your answer. [2]

6. Arthur wants to measure how fast a plant photosynthesises at different light intensities.
   The diagram shows the apparatus he uses.
   Arthur includes the following steps in his method:

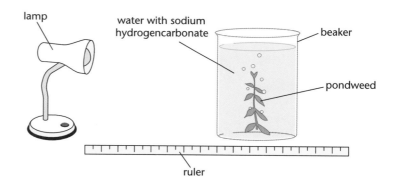

lamp

water with sodium hydrogencarbonate

beaker

pondweed

ruler

   • He uses the same piece of pondweed for the complete investigation.
   • He adds sodium hydrogencarbonate to the water to provide the plant with carbon dioxide.
   • He times five minutes using the minute hand of his watch and counts the number of bubbles given off.
   • He counts the bubbles three different times at each light intensity.
   • He repeats this with the light at different distances from the pondweed.
   (a) Why does Arthur choose pondweed for his experiment? [2]
   (b) What is the main gas found in the bubbles? [1]
   (c) Write down the step that:
       (i) helps to make Arthur's experiment a **fair test** [1]
       (ii) makes Arthur's experiment more **reliable**. [1]
   (d) Suggest one way that Arthur could make his experiment more **accurate**. [1]

2 Ecology

The following topics are covered in this chapter:

- ● **Food chains and energy flow**
- ● **Minerals and cycles**

2.1 Food chains and energy flow

Pyramids of biomass

 OCR B   B4e
AQA   B2.11.4

A food chain shows how food passes through a community of organisms. It enters the food chain as sunlight and is trapped by the producers. These are the green plants. The energy then passes from organism to organism as they eat each other.

> **Often the waste from one food chain can be used by decomposers to start another chain.**

The mass of all the organisms at each step of the food chain can be measured. This can be used to draw a diagram that is similar to a pyramid of numbers. The difference is that the area of each box represents the mass of all the organisms, not the number.

> **KEY POINT**   This type of diagram is called a pyramid of biomass.

foxes

rabbits

grass

Fig. 2.1 A pyramid of biomass.

The reason that a pyramid of biomass is shaped like a pyramid is that material and energy is lost from the food chain in different ways as the food is passed along.

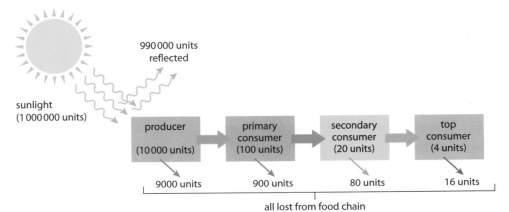

Fig. 2.2 Flow of energy through a food chain.

Fig. 2.2 shows that biomass and energy are lost from the food chain in a number of ways:

- In waste from the organisms. This is from excretion and egestion.
- As heat when organisms respire. Birds and mammals that keep a constant body temperature will often lose large amounts of energy in this way.

This loss of energy also explains why food chains usually only have four or five steps. By then there is so little energy left that animals would not be able to find enough food.

Intensive food production

The human population is increasing and so there is a greater demand for food. This means that many farmers now use **intensive farming** methods.

> **KEY POINT**
> Intensive farming means trying to obtain as much food as possible from the land, animals and plants.

Farmers use a number of intensive farming techniques to help increase their yield.

using pesticides to kill pests that might eat the crop

using herbicides to kill weeds that would compete with the crop

keep animals indoors so that they do not waste energy keeping warm or moving about

intensive farming

provide the plants with chemical fertilisers for growth

There are a number of different food production systems that use intensive methods:

Fish farming

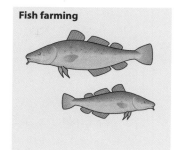

Fish are kept in enclosures away from predators. Their food supply and pests are controlled.

Glasshouses

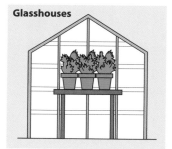

Plants can be grown in areas where the climate would not be suitable. They can also produce crops at different times of the year.

Hydroponics

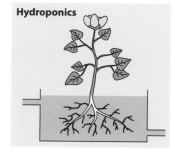

Plants are grown without soil. They need extra support but their mineral supply and pests are controlled.

Fig. 2.3 Food production systems that use intensive methods.

Organic food production

Many people think that intensive farming is harmful to the environment and cruel to animals. Farming that does not use the intensive methods is called **organic farming**.

Organic farming uses a number of different techniques:

Technique	Details
use of manure and compost	these provide minerals for the plant instead of using chemical fertilisers
crop rotation	farmers do not grow the same crop in a field year after year. This stops the build up of pests
use of nitrogen fixing crops	these crops contain bacteria that add minerals to the soil
weeding	this means that chemical herbicides are not needed
varying planting times	this can help to avoid times that pests are active
using biological control	farmers can use living organisms to help to control pests. They may eat them or cause disease

2.2 Minerals and cycles

Minerals and plants

For healthy growth, plants have to turn the glucose made in photosynthesis into many other chemicals. Some of these are shown on page 20.

To produce these chemicals, plants need various minerals from the soil:
- nitrates as a supply of nitrogen to make amino acids and proteins
- phosphates to supply phosphorus to make DNA and cell membranes
- potassium to help enzymes in respiration and photosynthesis
- magnesium to make chlorophyll.

Without these minerals, plants do not grow properly.

The minerals are taken up by the roots by active transport. This needs energy from respiration but it means that they can be taken up even if the concentration in the soil is very low.

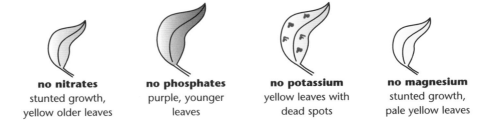

no nitrates
stunted growth, yellow older leaves

no phosphates
purple, younger leaves

no potassium
yellow leaves with dead spots

no magnesium
stunted growth, pale yellow leaves

Fig. 2.4 Lack of certain minerals is shown on a plant's leaves.

Decay

Some animals and plants die before they are eaten. They also produce large amounts of waste products. This waste material must be broken down or **decayed** because it contains useful minerals. If this did not happen, organisms would run out of minerals.

 KEY POINT Organisms that break down dead organic material are called decomposers.

The main organisms that act as decomposers are bacteria and fungi. They release enzymes on to the dead material to digest the large molecules. They then take up the soluble chemicals that are produced. The bacteria and fungi use the chemicals in respiration and for raw materials. This type of nutrition is called **saprophytic** and decomposers are sometimes called saprophytes.

For decomposers to decay dead material they need certain conditions:

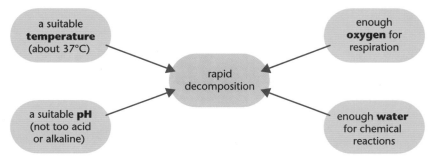

Some animals such as earthworms and woodlice are called **detritivores**. They feed on dead material and break it up into smaller pieces. This produces a larger surface area so decomposers can produce faster decay.

Fig. 2.5 An earthworm and woodlouse.

> **Gardeners try to produce ideal conditions for decay in their compost heaps.**

Although gardeners want decay to happen in compost heaps, people do not want their food to decay before they can eat it.

 KEY POINT Food preservation methods reduce the rate of decay of foods.

There are many ways to preserve food. Most stop decay by taking away one of the factors that decomposers need.

Preservation method	How it is done	How does it work?
canning	food is heated in a can and the can is sealed	the high temperature kills the microorganisms and oxygen cannot get into the can after it is sealed
cooling	food is kept in a refrigerator at about 5 °C	the growth and respiration of the decomposers slow down at low temperature
freezing	food is kept in a freezer at about −18 °C	the decomposers cannot respire or reproduce
drying	dry air is passed over the food	microorganisms cannot respire or reproduce without water
adding salt or sugar	food is soaked in a sugar solution or packed in salt	the sugar or salt draws water out of the decomposers
adding vinegar	the food is soaked in vinegar	the vinegar is too acidic for the decomposers

Nutrient cycles

It is possible to follow the way in which each mineral element passes through living organisms and becomes available again for use. Scientists use nutrient cycles to show how these minerals are recycled in nature.

Carbon dioxide is returned to the air in a number of different ways, but the main process that removes it from the air is photosynthesis.

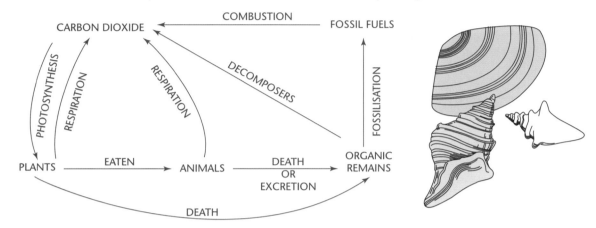

Fig. 2.6 The carbon cycle.

In the sea, carbon dioxide can also be locked up in the shells of animals. They can then form limestone. This can release carbon dioxide as it weathers or during volcanic eruption.

> **AQA candidates do not need to learn the nitrogen cycle.**

The nitrogen cycle is more complicated because, as well as the decomposers, it involves three other types of bacteria:

> **Although the air contains about 78% nitrogen it is unreactive. It needs lightning to make it react with oxygen.**

- **nitrifying bacteria** – these bacteria live in the soil and convert ammonium compounds to nitrates. They need oxygen to do this
- **denitrifying bacteria** – these bacteria in the soil are the enemy of farmers. They turn nitrates into nitrogen gas. They do not need oxygen
- **nitrogen fixing bacteria** – they live in the soil or in special bumps called nodules on the roots of plants from the pea and bean family. They take nitrogen gas and convert it back to useful nitrogen compounds.

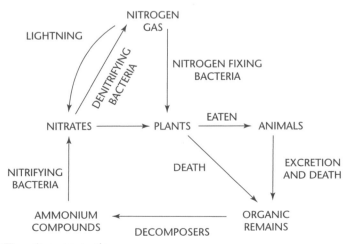

Fig. 2.7 The nitrogen cycle.

HOW SCIENCE WORKS

AQA B2.11.4
EDEXCEL 360 B2.3

Organic versus non-organic food

Organic food has now become big business. It is not necessary to go to special shops to buy organic food because all the major supermarkets have their own ranges of these foods. Sales of organic foods are increasing dramatically. Organic food sales have increased from just over £100 million in 1993/94 to £1.21 billion in 2004, more than £2 million a week.

But how do people know that food is organic?

The use of the term **organic**, when applied to food, has a legal meaning. It means the food has been grown and processed according to certain rules, known as Standards. These Standards cover every stage of organic food production, from farm to shop. These standards usually mean that organic food is dearer than non-organic food – but is it worth paying the extra money?

Some people think so, but others do not.

These two articles give two different points of view:

" Is it doing more harm than good? "

There is no doubt that much organic food is dearer than non-organic food.

For example, an organic chicken costs about £8.50 in a supermarket, almost three times the price of a non-organic chicken.

But some scientists now think that organic food could actually be harming the environment more than food grown using pesticides and fertilisers. A recent report says that some organic farming can create greater pollution and cause more global warming.

Scientists think that some foods such as organic milk, chicken and tomatoes need more energy and land for their production than non-organic foods.

'You cannot say that all organic food is better for the environment than all non-organic food,' said one of the scientists.

'If you look carefully at the amount of energy required to produce these foods, you get a complicated picture. In some cases, the carbon footprint for organic food is larger.'

The study looked at Britain's 150 top-selling foods. It studied the energy used to grow the food, along with processing and packaging. It also looked at the by-products from the farming.

It found that organic farming can cause some environmental problems. For example, because organic chickens take longer to grow than battery hens, they had a larger effect on the environment.

HOW SCIENCE WORKS

" It must be better for us "

There is no doubt that organic food is better for people and for the environment.

Organic food is grown without the using artificial pesticides and fertilisers. It has been known for some time that pesticides and fertilisers can stay on non-organic foods. They are eaten by people and, over long periods of time, these chemicals can build up in fatty tissues. They can then become dangerous. Although there have been no long-term studies about the difference between eating non-organic versus organic foods, it is obvious that organic food is better for you.

If you consider organic meat, it contains no antibiotics or growth hormones. All organic food contains no artificial additives, preservatives, colourings or flavourings and no hydrogenated fats. These fats can cause heart disease. The artificial additives in non-organic foods can make food last beyond its natural sell-by date, and make it look more colourful. At best, these additives are unnecessary and at worst, they may lead to cancer and could be causing damage that nobody has yet discovered.

Some people say that organic food can cause food poisoning. Organic food has not been linked to any case of food poisoning in any year since records began. But perhaps best of all, organic food tastes better and contains 50% more nutrients, minerals and vitamins than produce that has been intensively farmed.

HOW SCIENCE WORKS Questions

Try thinking about the answers to these questions:

1. The first article mentions 'scientists' and a 'report'? What effect do you think this has on people? **[2]**

2. Does the first article give a balanced argument? What does it concentrate on? **[2]**

3. Why do you think that people have such different views on this subject? **[2]**

Exam practice questions

1. The following substances are needed for plant growth.
    Match words **A**, **B**, **C**, and **D**, with the numbers **1–4** in the sentences.

    A auxins
    B carbon dioxide
    C nitrates
    D magnesium

    Plants need _____**1**_____ as the raw material for photosynthesis.
    They also need chlorophyll which contains the mineral _____**2**_____
    To grow plants need to convert sugars into proteins using _____**3**_____
    The growth of the plant is controlled by _____**4**_____   **[4]**

2. The table contains some farming methods.
    Put an (✓) next to any method that would **not** be used by organic farmers.

Spreading manure on the fields	
Spraying chemical pesticides	
Killing weeds using weedkillers	
Rotating their crops	

    [2]

3. The boxes contain some bacteria found in the nitrogen cycle and some roles.
    Draw straight lines to join each **bacteria** to its correct **role**.

    Bacteria

    nitrogen fixing bacteria

    decomposing bacteria

    nitrifying bacteria

    denitrifying bacteria

    Role

    break down organic remains

    convert ammonium compounds to nitrates

    convert nitrate to nitrogen gas

    convert nitrogen gas to nitrogen compounds

    [3]

Exam practice questions

4. The diagram shows the flow of energy along a food chain.

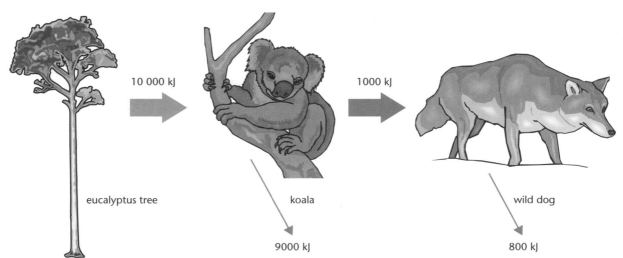

For every 10 000 kJ that the koala bear takes in it uses 1000 kJ for growth.

(a) What is the percentage efficiency of this transfer? **[1]**

(b) Write down one way that energy is lost from this food chain. **[1]**

(c) Work out how much energy the wild dog uses for growth. **[1]**

(d) This food chain contains three organisms.
Explain why food chains rarely have more that five organisms. **[2]**

(e) The eucalyptus tree loses a small number of leaves all the year round.
These leaves fall onto the soil.
Explain how the carbon in these leaves become available again to the tree. **[4]**

5. Read the How Science Works article about organic farming and answer these questions.

(a) The boxes contain some statements from the article.
Put the letter F next to any statements that are facts and C next to any that are conclusions.

Sales of organic foods are increasing dramatically	
Organic food is better for people	
Much organic food is dearer than intensively produced food	
Organic food tastes better than non-organic food	
Artificial additives can make food look more colourful	

[3]

(b) The article states that there have been no long term studies about the difference between eating organic and non-organic food.
Why do you think that the sale of organic food is increasing so much? **[2]**

(c) Some people think that all food should be grown organically in all countries.
Suggest and explain **one** problem that this may cause. **[2]**

Further physiology

The following topics are covered in this chapter:

- **Homeostasis**
- **Digestion**
- **Transport in plants and animals**
- **Nerves, synapses and the brain**

3.1 Homeostasis

Principles of homeostasis

 OCR A — B4.1
 AQA — B2.11.7

> **KEY POINT**
> It is vital that the internal environment of the body is kept fairly constant. This is called homeostasis.

The different factors that need to be kept constant include:

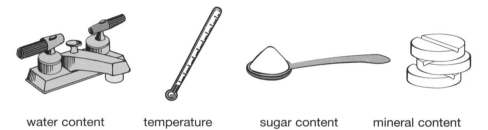

water content   temperature   sugar content   mineral content

The body has a number of automatic control systems that keep these factors at steady levels. This is important for cells to function properly.

These control systems work in the same sort of way as some artificial systems, such as the temperature control in a house.

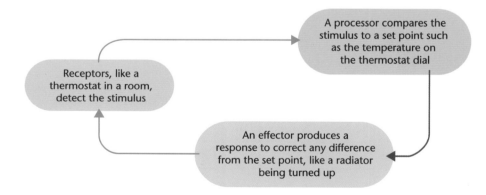

A processor compares the stimulus to a set point such as the temperature on the thermostat dial

Receptors, like a thermostat in a room, detect the stimulus

An effector produces a response to correct any difference from the set point, like a radiator being turned up

> **KEY POINT**
> This kind of system that detects any change and corrects it, is called negative feedback.

Systems that work against each other are called antagonistic.

Some systems have more than one effector that can work in opposite directions. This means that the response can happen much faster. This is like turning the radiators up and down, and also opening or closing the windows.

Control of body temperature

OCR A   B4.1
AQA   B2.11.7

Like many factors in the body, it is important to make sure that heat gain and loss are balanced, otherwise the body temperature will change.

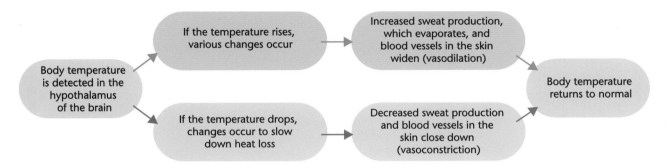

The body also has temperature receptors in the skin. These tell the brain about the external temperature so any changes in body temperature can be predicted.

Sometimes when we are ill, or in extreme conditions, temperature control can go wrong in several ways.

Heat stroke

- This is an uncontrolled increase in body temperature.
- It is caused by extreme exercise or very hot conditions.
- It can cause headaches, sickness and dizziness.
- The person should be cooled down and given liquid to stop dehydration which otherwise would stop the person sweating and increase the temperature.

Hypothermia

- This happens when the body temperature falls below 35 °C.
- The person shivers violently and may be confused.
- They should be kept warm with dry blankets.

Control of blood sugar

AQA   B2.11.7

It is vital that the sugar or glucose level of the blood is kept constant. This job is performed by the **pancreas**.

> **KEY POINT**
>
> **Insulin is the hormone that controls the level of glucose in the blood.**

When glucose levels are too high, the pancreas makes more insulin. This allows more glucose to move into the cells from the blood.

Diabetics do not produce enough insulin naturally. They need regular insulin injections in order to control the level of glucose in their blood. They also need to control their diet carefully.

Control of water balance

OCR A   **B4.4**

The **kidneys** remove waste such as urea from the body. They also control the water balance of the body.

The kidneys do this in the following way:
- they filter the blood to remove all small molecules
- they reabsorb useful molecules such as sugar, back into the blood
- then a certain amount of water and salts are taken back into the blood to keep their levels in balance
- the remaining waste is stored in the bladder as urine.

The amount of water that is taken back into the blood is controlled by a hormone called **ADH** which is released by the **pituitary gland**.

| Warm temperatures, exercise, salt intake or lack of fluids | → | The blood becomes too concentrated | → | The pituitary gland releases more ADH | → | More water is reabsorbed and a more concentrated urine is made |

Different drugs can alter ADH release. **Alcohol** reduces ADH release and can cause too much urine to be made. **Ecstasy** can cause the opposite effect.

3.2 Transport in plants and animals

Blood and the heart

OCR B   **B3c**

The blood is made up of a liquid called **plasma**. This carries chemicals such as hormones, antibodies and waste products around the body.

Cells are also carried in the plasma. They are adapted for different jobs.

> **KEY POINT**
> Red blood cells contain haemoglobin which can carry oxygen around the body.

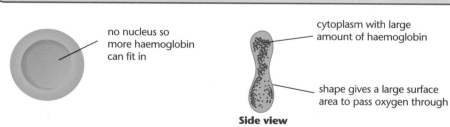

no nucleus so more haemoglobin can fit in

cytoplasm with large amount of haemoglobin

shape gives a large surface area to pass oxygen through

Side view

Fig. 3.1 A red blood cell.

> **KEY POINT**
> White blood cells can change shape to engulf and destroy disease organisms.

The blood is carried around the body in arteries, veins and capillaries.

Arteries	Veins	Capillaries
carry blood away from the heart	carry blood back to the heart	join arteries to veins
have thick, muscular walls because the blood is under high pressure	have valves and a wide lumen because the blood is under low pressure	have permeable walls so that substances can pass in and out to the tissues

A double circulation keeps the pressure higher so the blood flows faster.

KEY POINT

In mammals, the blood vessels are arranged in a double circulation. This means that the blood is sent to the lungs and then returns to the heart before being pumped to the body.

This means that the heart has to deal with oxygenated and deoxygenated blood at the same time. The two types of blood are kept separate in different sides of the heart.

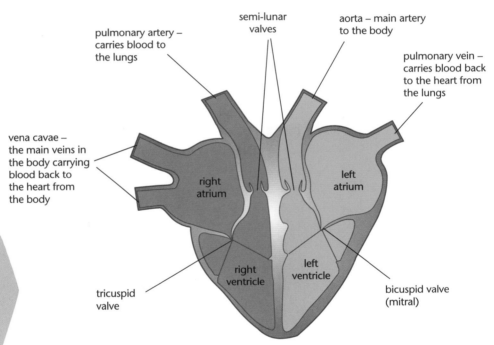

Notice that the wall of the left ventricle is thicker than the right ventricle. This is because it has to pump the blood further.

Fig. 3.2 Cross section of a heart.

Because the heart is such an important organ, any problems that occur are very serious. A type of fat called cholesterol can build up in the blood vessels that supply the heart muscle. This can cause areas of heart muscle to die. The heart valves may also be damaged by disease. Some people may need a new valve or even a new heart. Some artificial replacements are available but have drawbacks. Human organs for donation are in short supply and they may also lead to rejection problems.

Transport in plants

OCR B   B3c

Plants have two different tissues that are used to transport substances. They are called **xylem** and **phloem**.

Xylem	Phloem
carries water and minerals from roots to the leaves	carries dissolved food substances both up and down the plant
the movement of water up the plant and out of the leaves is called **transpiration**	the movement of the dissolved food is called **translocation**
made of vessels which are hollow tubes consisting of thickened dead cells	made of columns of living cells

Water movement in plants

- Water enters the plant through the root hairs, by osmosis. It then passes from cell to cell, by osmosis until it reaches the centre of the root.
- The water enters xylem vessels in the root, and then travels up the stem.
- Water enters the leaves and evaporates. It then passes through the **stomata** by **diffusion**. This loss of water by transpiration helps to pull water up the xylem vessels.

How fast does transpiration happen?

The rate of transpiration depends on a number of factors:

- **temperature** – warm weather increases the kinetic energy of the water molecules so they move out of the leaf faster
- **humidity** – damp air reduces the concentration gradient so the water molecules leave the leaf more slowly
- **wind** – the wind blows away the water molecules so that a large diffusion gradient is maintained
- **light** – light causes the stomata to open and so more water is lost.

Why do plants lose water?

When plants are short of water, they do not want to waste it through transpiration. The trouble is they need to let carbon dioxide in, so water will always be able to get out. Water loss is kept as low as possible in several ways:

- Photosynthesis only occurs during the day, so the stomata close at night to reduce water loss.
- The stomata are placed on the underside of the leaf. This reduces water loss because they are away from direct sunlight and protected from the wind.
- The top surface of the leaf, facing the Sun, is often covered with a protective waxy layer.

Although transpiration is kept as low as possible, it does help plants by cooling them down and supplying leaves with minerals. It also provides water for support and photosynthesis.

3.3 Digestion

Digestion

AQA   B2.11.6

Most **enzymes** work inside cells controlling reactions. Some enzymes pass out of cells and work in the digestive system. These enzymes digest our food, making the molecules small enough to be absorbed.

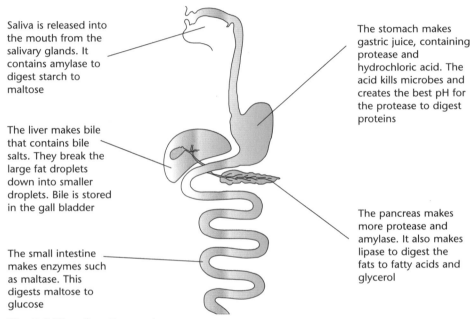

Saliva is released into the mouth from the salivary glands. It contains amylase to digest starch to maltose

The liver makes bile that contains bile salts. They break the large fat droplets down into smaller droplets. Bile is stored in the gall bladder

The small intestine makes enzymes such as maltase. This digests maltose to glucose

The stomach makes gastric juice, containing protease and hydrochloric acid. The acid kills microbes and creates the best pH for the protease to digest proteins

The pancreas makes more protease and amylase. It also makes lipase to digest the fats to fatty acids and glycerol

Fig. 3.3 The digestive system.

3.4 Nerves, synapses and the brain

Nerves, synapses and the brain

OCR A   B6.1–6

All living organisms need to respond to changes in the environment.

Although this happens in different ways, the pattern of events is always the same:

stimulus → detection → co-ordination → response

 KEY POINT **The job of receptors is to detect the stimulus and effectors bring about the response.**

It is the job of nerve cells to carry the messages around the body.
- **Sensory neurones** carry impulses from receptors to the CNS.
- **Motor neurones** carry impulses from the CNS to effectors.

Synapses

Each neurone does not directly end on another neurone.

There is a small gap between the two neurones and this is called a **synapse**.

In order for an impulse to be generated in the next neurone a **chemical transmitter** is released. This then diffuses across the small gap.

Many drugs work by interfering with synapses. They may block or copy the action of neurotransmitters in certain neurones.

Ecstasy (MDMA) works by increasing the neurotransmitter **serotonin** in the brain. This increase in serotonin causes a change in mood.

Reflexes

Reflexes are responses that do not involve conscious thought. There are two main types.

Simple reflexes:
- produce a rapid response
- examples include the control of pupil size, many responses in newborn babies and much of the behaviour of simple animals.

Conditioned reflexes:
- this happens when an organism learns to link one stimulus with another stimulus, e.g. Pavlov's dogs
- the response therefore has no direct link with the stimulus
- they help organisms to avoid harm, e.g. birds avoid caterpillars that are a certain colour.

Memory and the brain

The brain contains billions of neurones and the **cerebral cortex** is the part of the brain involved with intelligence, memory, language and consciousness.

Scientists can work out the jobs of each part of the cortex by looking at patients with brain damage and using MRI scans.

Mammals **learn** from experiences by making new connections between neurones. This makes new nerve pathways which are more likely to be used in the future. This is the basis of **memories**.

People are more likely to remember things if:
- the stimulus is repeated a number of times
- if there is a pattern in the information
- if there is a strong stimulus, such as a smell, associated with it.

There are some skills that can only be learnt up to a particular age. Children can only learn some language skills up to a certain age.

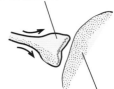

1 Impulse arrives

Synaptic knob of neurone A

cell body of neurone B

2 Chemical secreted into minute gap (synapse)

3 New impulse generated by neurone B

Chemical destroyed by enzymes

Fig. 3.4 Synaptic transmission.

HOW SCIENCE WORKS

Organ donation

Organ transplants involve the donation of organs from one person to another. Every year in the UK, about 2700 people receive a transplant. Transplants are sometimes the only treatment for certain patients. Attempts have been made to make mechanical replacements for organs, with little success.

Kidney transplants are the most common, but transplants of the heart, liver and lungs are also regularly carried out. Other tissues such as corneas, heart valves, skin and bone can also be donated. As medical techniques have improved, more and more patients can be considered for transplants. This has led to a major problem, a serious shortage of donors.

For some people this means waiting for a long time and some may die before a suitable organ becomes available.

The line on the graph shows the number of people in the UK on the transplant list. The bars show the number of people who died and became donors and the number of transplants performed.

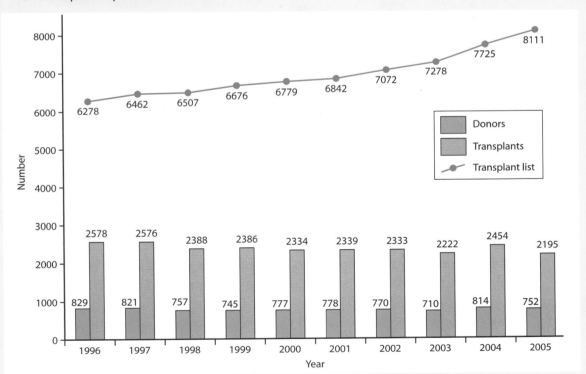

"Statistics prepared by UK Transplant from the National Transplant Database maintained on behalf of transplant services in the UK and Republic of Ireland."

UK transplant statistics can be found at
http://www.uktransplant.org.uk/ukt/statistics/statistics.jsp
UK Transplant is part of NHS Blood and Transplant (NHSBT)

HOW SCIENCE WORKS

This article describes a recent idea to try and make more organs available for transplants.

A bid to boost organ donation has recently been rejected by MPs. The current system only allows organs to be removed if a person carries a donor card. Relatives of the person can stop the organs being taken even if the person is carrying a card. A recent survey showed 70% of British adults questioned are willing to donate their organs but many do not carry a card. The new system would mean that organs can be taken from a person unless they have opted not to allow it. This is called presumed consent.

Supporters of this new system say:

This would greatly increase the numbers of organs available for transplants.

When somebody dies it is very difficult to ask relatives about donation.

In opt-out schemes already running, only 2% of people decide they do not want to donate their organs.

The Presumed Consent scheme solves most of these problems. It forces people to make a decision.

People who are against the new idea say:

Not everyone is happy with the idea of transplants. There are people who have religious and cultural objections.

They might not realise that they need to opt out and could have their organs used.

Mistakes could also be made and people could have their organs taken by mistake even if they have opted out. Getting it wrong could lead to distress for relatives and could lead to a backlash against doctors and organ donation.

HOW SCIENCE WORKS *Questions*

1. Look at the graph.
   (a) Describe what patterns it shows.
   (b) Explain how it highlights the need for more organs for transplants. **[2]**
2. Deciding about transplants involves a number of difficult ethical questions, what do you think?
   (a) Do you think the 'presumed consent' system should be introduced?
   (b) Is it right that many people receive organ transplants but do not carry donor cards themselves?
   (c) If there are a limited number of organs available, how do doctors decide which patients should receive transplants? **[6]**

Exam practice questions

1. The following structures are involved in transport in plants.
    Match words **A**, **B**, **C**, and **D**, with the numbers **1–4** in the sentences.

    A   stomata
    B   xylem
    C   phloem
    D   root hairs

    Plants take water up from the soil. Plants have many _____**1**_____ to increase their surface area for water uptake.
    The water is carried up the stem in the _____**2**_____
    Sugars, however, are transported in the _____**3**_____
    Water is lost to the air through _____**4**_____   **[4]**

2. Put a tick (✓) next to any processes that are likely to occur in a person when their blood gets too hot.

Their muscles contract uncontrollably	
The blood vessels in the skin widen	
The sweat gland becomes less active	
The pituitary gland releases less ADH	

    [2]

3. The boxes contain some blood vessels and some descriptions.
    Draw straight lines to join each **blood vessel** to the correct **description**.

    Blood vessel

    aorta

    pulmonary artery

    pulmonary vein

    vena cava

    Description

    carries oxygenated blood under low pressure

    carries blood into the right atrium

    carries deoxygenated blood away from the heart

    carries oxygenated blood under high pressure   **[3]**

Exam practice questions

4. The graph shows the levels of glucose and insulin in Alysha's blood.
The readings were taken for 60 minutes after Alysha had eaten a meal of rice.

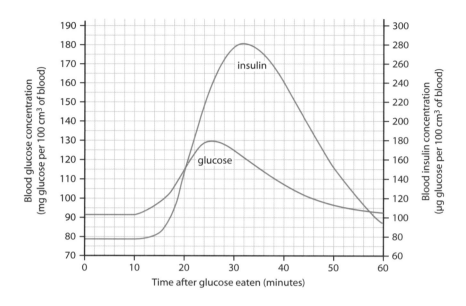

(a) Rice contains a high quantity of starch.
Describe how and where this starch is digested in the body. **[3]**

(b) **(i)** How long does it take for the blood glucose levels to rise after the meal? **[1]**
(ii) Give two reasons why it takes some time for the glucose levels to rise. **[2]**

(c) **(i)** What is the maximum level of insulin in the blood during the experiment? **[1]**
(ii) Explain why insulin levels rise after the meal. **[3]**

(d) How would you expect the two lines on the graph to be different if Alysha has diabetes? **[2]**

5. Read the How Science Works pages about organ donation and answer the following questions.

(a) The article states that it is difficult to produce mechanical replacements for many organs.
Suggest one reason why. **[1]**

(b) The table contains some arguments about the idea of presumed consent.
Put a (✓) next to any statements that could be used to argue for presumed consent.

Some people's organs could be removed in error	
It would increase the number of organs available for transplants	
It would avoid having to ask relatives about donation	
Some people have religious objections to transplants	

[2]

(c) According to the article, 70% of people in the UK say that they are willing to donate organs but do not carry donor cards.
Suggest two reasons why this might be. **[2]**

Genes and biotechnology

The following topics are covered in this chapter:

- **Inheriting genes**
- **Biotechnology**
- **Using our knowledge of genes**

4.1 Inheriting genes

Inheriting genes

We have two copies of each chromosome in our cells (one from each parent) which means that we have two copies of each gene.

> **KEY POINT**
>
> **A copy of a gene is called an allele.**

Sometimes the two alleles are the same, but sometimes they are different.

A good example of this is tongue rolling. This is controlled by a single gene and there are two copies or alleles of the gene, one that says roll and the other that says do not roll.

> **People that are non-rollers must have two recessive alleles.**

But because we have two alleles, if one says roll and the other says do not roll, then a person can still roll their tongue. This is because the allele for rolling is dominant and the non-rolling allele is recessive.

How to work out the results of a cross

We usually give the alleles letters, with the dominant allele a capital letter. For example, T = tongue rolling and t = non-rolling.

Let us assume that mum cannot roll her tongue but dad can.

Both of dad's alleles are T so he is homozygous.

The cross is usually drawn out like this:

> **In this cross, all the children can roll their tongue.**

		mum	
		t	t
dad	T	Tt	Tt
	T	Tt	Tt

All are tongue rollers

If both mum and dad are heterozygous, the children that they can produce will be different:

		mum	
		T	t
dad	T	Tt	Tt
	t	Tt	tt

Cannot roll tongue

Inherited disorders

Many genetic disorders are caused by certain alleles. These can be passed on from mother or father to the baby and lead to the baby having the disorder. Examples of these disorders are cystic fibrosis and Huntington's disorder.

KEY POINT Cystic fibrosis is caused by a recessive allele and Huntington's is caused by a dominant allele.

By looking at family trees of these genetic disorders and drawing genetic diagrams like the one for tongue rolling, it is possible for people to know the chance of them having a child with a genetic disorder. This may leave them with a difficult decision to make as to whether to have a child or not.

Remember, genetic cross diagrams can only work out the probability of a child being affected.

Sex determination

AQA B2.11.8

Humans have 23 pairs of **chromosomes**. The chromosomes of one of these pairs are called the sex chromosomes because they carry the genes that determine the sex of the person.

KEY POINT There are two kinds of sex chromosome. One is called X and one is called Y.

- Females have two X chromosomes and are XX.
- Males have an X and a Y chromosome and are XY.

It is possible to separate X and Y sperm in the laboratory and so choose the sex of a baby.

This means that females produce ova that contain single X chromosomes and males produce sperm, half of which contain a Y chromosome and half of which contain an X chromosome.

	X	Y
X	XX	XY
X	XX	XY

4.2 *Using our knowledge of genes*

Genetic fingerprints

Scientists have discovered that our DNA contains regions that do not code for proteins. This is often called junk DNA. In this DNA are regions with repeating sequences that can be used to identify each individual.

> **KEY POINT**
>
> **A genetic fingerprint is a pattern of DNA that can be used to identify an individual.**

Step 1 – the regions of the DNA are isolated and cut up using enzymes.

Step 2 – the DNA fragments are put on a gel and separated using an electric current.

Step 3 – the fragments are treated with a radioactive probe so that the bands of DNA can be photographed.

Selective breeding

> **KEY POINT**
>
> **Selective breeding involves choosing animals or plants with desired characteristics and allowing them to breed.**

Selective breeding is not new; farmers have been altering the genes of their plants and animals for thousands of years. For example, to produce larger hens' eggs, farmers bred the hens that produced the largest eggs, with cocks hatched from large eggs. They repeated this for several generations. Other examples include: breeds of dogs, higher yielding crops with better flavour and resistance to disease.

There are problems with selective breeding:
● the animals all become too closely related or inbred
● the process can take a long time.

A quicker way of changing the genes of animals or plants is **genetic engineering**.

Genetic engineering

> **KEY POINT**
> Genetic engineering involves taking DNA from one organism and putting it into the chromosomes of another organism.

When scientists investigated the genetic code, they found that all living organisms use the same code. This makes it possible to move genes from one organism to another and it can even be to an organism of another species; from a person to a bacterium, for example.

A number of steps in the process involve using enzymes:

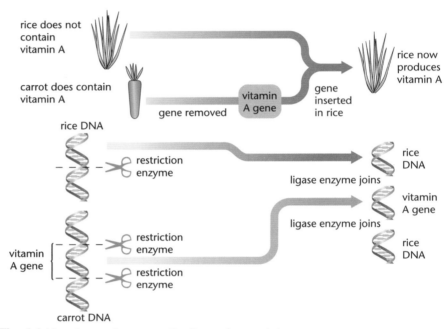

Fig. 4.1 How to produce genetically engineered rice.

People often have different views about genetic engineering.
- Some people think that genetic engineering is against 'God and Nature' and is potentially dangerous.
- Some people think that genetic engineering will provide massive benefits to mankind, like better food and less disease.

This is discussed further on pages 53 & 54.

There is also the possibility that genetic engineering may be used to treat genetic disorders like cystic fibrosis. Scientists are trying to replace the genes in people that have the disorder with working genes.

> **KEY POINT**
> Using genetic engineering to treat genetic disorders is called gene therapy.

Again this is quite controversial because it could be used to change the genes of embryos. People are worried that it might be used to produce 'designer babies'.

4.3 Biotechnology

Useful microorganisms

Microorganisms have been used for hundreds of years for making foods such as bread and cheese. They are now being used more and more to produce new types of food and other useful products.

> **KEY POINT** The use of living organisms to make useful products is called **biotechnology**.

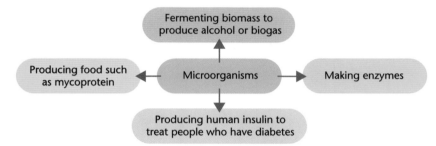

Microorganisms can be grown in large vessels called **fermenters**. The conditions are carefully controlled so that the microorganisms grow very fast. Like all organisms, they need food to obtain energy but they can often be fed on waste from other processes.

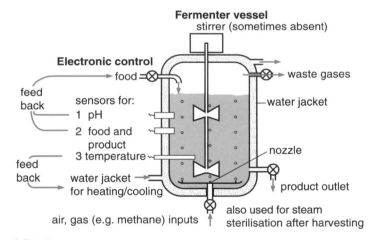

Fig. 4.2 A fermenter.

The microorganisms can be fed on **biomass** such as manure or plant material. The ethanol or biogas that is produced can be used as a fuel.

The **enzymes** that some microorganisms make can be used for a number of different processes:

- protein and fat digesting enzymes (proteases and lipases can be used in washing powders)
- carbohydrases can be used to convert starch into sugar syrup
- isomerase can be used to convert the sugar glucose into fructose which is much sweeter.

HOW SCIENCE WORKS

OCRB B3g
EDEXCEL 360 B2.2

Vitamin A

Vitamin A is a fat-soluble vitamin. The best sources of vitamin A are eggs, milk, butter and fish. Plants do not contain vitamin A, but they contain beta-carotene. Beta-carotene can be converted to vitamin A in the body. The best sources of beta-carotene are dark-green, orange, and yellow vegetables. Cereals are poor sources of beta-carotene.

Vitamin A is used for two functions in the body. In the eye, it is needed to make light sensitive cells for seeing in dim light. Vitamin A is also important during the development of the embryo.

Vitamin A deficiency is common in areas like Southeast Asia, where polished rice, which lacks the vitamin, is a major part of the diet. The earliest symptom of vitamin A deficiency is night blindness. Continued vitamin A deficiency leads to inflammation and infection in the eye, resulting in total and irreversible blindness. Vitamin A deficiency can be prevented or treated by taking vitamin supplements or eating food rich in vitamin A. In Africa, Indonesia, and the Philippines, programmes supply children with injections of the vitamin. However, figures show that 500 000 children go blind each year due to vitamin A deficiency.

It has also been shown that children can be born with a number of different birth defects if their mother lacked vitamin A when she was pregnant.

So should everybody take vitamin A tablets?

We have to be careful because studies have shown that too much vitamin A may be dangerous. There have been lots of different studies, but some studies are better designed than others.

Look at this study:

- In a recent study, scientists questioned over 22 000 women.
- They asked them about their eating habits and which vitamin tablets they took before and during pregnancy. This was used to see how much vitamin A they ingested.
- They then counted the numbers of any birth defects in the babies.
- They concluded that vitamin A was dangerous because the total number of different defects increased as vitamin A intake increased.

Golden rice

Due to the number of people with vitamin A deficiency, scientists have been developing genetically modified rice rich in beta-carotene. The idea is that this will help people who can't afford a diet containing enough natural sources of vitamin A. The Golden Rice project is one project and is already undergoing trials. Different groups have different views on this project.

HOW SCIENCE WORKS

I think that the introduction of golden rice would be a real mistake. A person would have to eat about twelve times the amount of rice that they eat now to have any effect. I also think that it is wrong to introduce this rice because it might make people dependent on one food only. They might start to suffer from other deficiency diseases. It would be better to spend money introducing many vitamin-rich food plants that are cheap and already available.

Anyway I think there are dangers with any genetically introduced crops. We do not really know how safe the Golden Rice is. It could also breed with wild relatives to contaminate wild rice forever. If there were any problems, the clock could not be turned back.

I think that the use of Golden Rice is a real step forward. We have tried other methods but there are still 500 000 children a year going blind. It is time to try something new. If this method works then the gene could be put into other crops like sweet potatoes and cassava. If it works with vitamin A then genes for other vitamins or amino acids could be introduced. I don't think that they will have to eat large amounts to see an effect. The figure of twelve times the dose may be an ideal amount but improvements will be seen by eating smaller amounts.

HOW SCIENCE WORKS Questions

When any new scientific study is performed it should be a **fair test** and obtain data that is **accurate** and **reliable**.

Look at the study on vitamin A and pregnant women.

(a) Do you think it was a fair test? [1]

(b) Do you think the method for measuring vitamin A intake was accurate? [1]

Exam practice questions

1. The following processes involve manipulating genes.
    Match words **A**, **B**, **C**, and **D**, with the numbers **1–4** in the sentences.

    A   genetic engineering
    B   gene therapy
    C   selective breeding
    D   genetic fingerprinting

    Farmers have been manipulating the genes of their animals by choosing which animals mate. This is called _____1_____

    It is now possible to make bacteria produce human insulin by the process of _____2_____

    If a person's genes are altered to cure a disease this is called _____3_____

    A scientist may use _____4_____ to identify a person from a sample of their cells.   **[4]**

2. The diagram shows some stages in the production of human insulin by bacteria.

    A   insulin gene
    bacterial chromosome

    B   bacterium
    chromosome

    C

    D   human DNA
    insulin gene

    (a)   Write down the order that the steps would take place.
    The first one has been done for you.

    ___D___   _____   _____   _____   **[2]**

    (b)   The table contains some statements about this method of making insulin.
    Put an (**X**) next to any incorrect statements.

The process uses hormones to cut DNA	
The bacteria can be grown in large fermenters	
The insulin produced is a hybrid of human and bacterial insulin	
The bacteria can be grown on cheap waste products	

    [2]

Exam practice questions

3. **(a)** The boxes contain some parts of a fermenter and their jobs.
Draw straight lines to join each part to its correct job.

Part	Job
steam inlet	to keep a constant temperature in the fermenter
water jacket	to mix the microorganism with the food
stirrer	to allow the microrganism to respire
air inlet	to sterilise the fermenter between batches

[3]

(b) Fermenters that produce biogas are often used in remote areas of countries.

(i) Write down **one** raw material that can be used to produce biogas. **[1]**

(ii) Write down **two** advantages of using biogas as a fuel, rather than fossil fuels. **[2]**

4. Read the How Science Works article and use it to answer the following questions.

(a) Look at these possible changes to the vitamin A and pregnant women study.

A Question more than 22 000 women.
B Measure vitamin A intake by taking regular blood samples.
C Study women in different countries.

(i) Which of these changes would make the data from the vitamin A and pregnant women study more **accurate**? **[1]**

(ii) Which of these changes would make the data from the vitamin A and pregnant women study more **reliable**? **[1]**

(b) The study judged the danger of vitamin A by simply counting the number of any defects.
Is this a valid way of judging the danger of high vitamin A levels? **[2]**

(c) The two people have different views on how much Golden Rice a person needs to eat to have an effect.
Why do you think their views differ? **[2]**

The following topics are covered in this chapter:

● **Atoms**
● **Bonding**

5.1 Atoms

What is inside an atom?

OCR A | C4.2
OCR B | C3a
AQA | C2.12.1
EDEXCEL 360 | C2 6

Matter is made up of tiny particles called **atoms**. Atoms are the basic building blocks of matter.

> **KEY POINT**
> **Atoms are the smallest particles of an element that can still have the chemical properties of that element.**

Atoms of all the elements are made up of three different particles: **protons**, **neutrons** and **electrons**.

These particles are smaller than the atoms themselves. We call them sub-atomic particles.

Particle	Symbol	Mass (atomic mass unit u)	Charge
proton	p	1	+1
electron	e	$\frac{1}{1840}$	−1
neutron	n	1	0 (neutral)

Most of an atom is empty space. If a football stadium represented an atom, the nucleus would be the size of a pea.

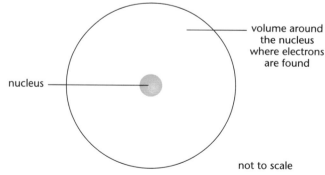

Fig. 5.1 The structure of an atom.

You can see in Fig. 5.1 above that an atom consists of a nucleus and electrons that move around the nucleus. The nucleus contains protons and neutrons only. An atom has no overall charge because the number of protons is equal to the number of electrons.

Protons and neutrons are collectively called **nucleons**.

Elements

 KEY POINT An element is a pure substance that cannot be split up into two or more simpler substances by physical or chemical processes.

- An element is made of only one type of atom. Each element has its own type of atom. This means that the atoms of one element are not the same as the atoms of another element.
- There are 92 naturally occurring elements. Oxygen, hydrogen, nitrogen, sulfur, iron, copper, titanium and silver are examples of elements.
- Sugar is not an element. When heated, sugar decomposes to give water and carbon.
- Water is not an element. It can be broken down to give hydrogen and oxygen atoms.
- Carbon, hydrogen and oxygen are elements because they cannot be further broken down into simpler substances.
- Chemists use chemical symbols as abbreviations for the names of elements. Each symbol consists of one or two letters.

KEY POINT All elements have their own symbols that may consist of one or two letters.

Atomic number

 KEY POINT The number of protons in an atom is called the atomic number. It is represented by the symbol Z.

The number of protons in an atom is also called the proton number.

Since atoms are neutral, the atomic number is also the number of electrons in the atom.

Each different element has its own proton number.

- Carbon has a proton number of 6. All atoms with six protons are carbon atoms.
- Oxygen has a proton number of 8. All atoms with eight protons are oxygen atoms.

Mass number

 KEY POINT The number of protons and neutrons in an atom is called the mass number. It is also called the nucleon number. It is represented by the letter A.

The electrons in an atom have negligible mass and do not contribute significantly to the mass of the atom.

- Nucleon number (A) = total number of protons and neutrons in an atom
- Number of neutrons = nucleon number (A) – proton number (Z)

The nucleon number of an element is often shown as a superscript to the left of the symbol for the element; the proton number as a subscript also to the left.

The example shows an atom of sodium.

nucleon number A$\rightarrow$ $^{23}_{11}$Na $\leftarrow$ symbol of element
proton number Z$\nearrow$

For convenience, the element is sometimes represented by using only the nucleon number e.g. sodium–23 or ^{23}Na.

Isotopes

The atoms of an element are not always identical. For example, there are three types of hydrogen atoms. They all contain the same number of protons and electrons, but a different number of neutrons. These are called isotopes of hydrogen.

Isotope	Symbol	No. of protons	No. of electrons	No. of neutrons
hydrogen-1 (hydrogen)	H	1	1	0
hydrogen-2 (deuterium)	D	1	1	1
hydrogen-3 (tritium)	T	1	1	2

D_2O is known as 'heavy water'.

Hydrogen is the only element that has different names for its isotopes.

> **KEY POINT**
> Isotopes are atoms of the same element with the same number of protons but different number of neutrons.

Another way of defining isotopes is as atoms that have the same proton number but different nucleon numbers.

There are two chlorine isotopes. A sample of chlorine consists of chlorine–35 and chlorine–37 in approximately 3 to 1 ratio. This explains the fact that the relative atomic mass of naturally occurring chlorine is approximately 35.5.

> **KEY POINT**
> The relative atomic mass of an element is the mass of an 'average atom' compared with the mass of a carbon atom.

A few of the elements have only one type of atom. Fluorine–19 is the only isotope of fluorine.

- Isotopes have the same chemical properties, but differ slightly in their physical properties.
- The chemical properties of isotopes are similar because chemical reactions involve only the electrons and **not** the protons and neutrons.
- The physical properties will differ because the atomic masses of the isotopes differ. For example hydrogen–2 has a slightly higher boiling point and density than hydrogen–l.

The electronic arrangement of atoms

OCR B | C3a
AQA | C2.12.3
EDEXCEL 360 | C2 6

The atom is about 100 000 times bigger than its nucleus. If a table tennis ball (radius about 2 cm) is used to represent the nucleus of an atom, then the first electron would be found about 2 km from the ball.

Electrons move rapidly and orbit round the nucleus. The electrons are found at relatively great distances away from the nucleus.

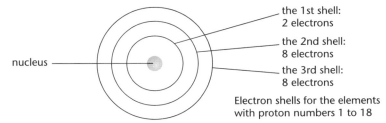

the 1st shell: 2 electrons

the 2nd shell: 8 electrons

the 3rd shell: 8 electrons

nucleus

Electron shells for the elements with proton numbers 1 to 18

Fig. 5.2 Electron shells for the elements with proton numbers 1 to 18.

● The way in which the electrons are arranged around the nucleus of an atom is very important because *it is this electron arrangement that determines the chemical properties of the atom.*

The electrons in an atom move around the nucleus in clearly defined regions called electron shells. Each electron shell is capable of holding only a certain number of electrons.

The first shell is closest to the nucleus and can hold a maximum of two electrons. This shell is always filled first because it is the lowest energy shell.

The second and third shell can contain up to eight electrons each. The shells fill up in sequence before the next shell is started.

The atomic structures of a hydrogen atom and a magnesium atom are:

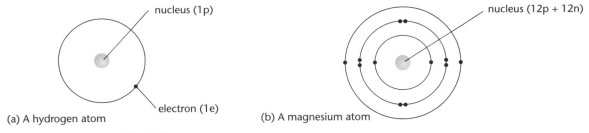

nucleus (1p)

electron (1e)

(a) A hydrogen atom

nucleus (12p + 12n)

(b) A magnesium atom

Fig. 5.3 Atoms.

KEY POINT The way the electrons are arranged in an atom is called its electronic structure or **electronic configuration**.

A magnesium atom (atomic number 12) has two electrons in the first shell, eight electrons in the second shell and two electrons in the third shell. Its electronic configuration can be represented as (2,8,2).

Valence electrons

Electronic arrangement is extremely important in Chemistry. The chemical properties of an element depend on the number of electrons in the outer shell. For example, sodium (2,8,1) and potassium (2,8,8,1) have similar properties because their electronic configurations are similar. In each case, there is one electron in the outer shell.

The shell that is furthest from the nucleus is called the **outer shell**. The electrons in this shell are called **valence electrons**.

The electronic configurations of the first 20 elements are shown on page 79.

The stability of the noble gas structure

The noble gases are helium (He), neon (Ne), argon (Ar), krypton (Kr) and xenon (Xe). The electronic configurations of helium, neon and argon are:

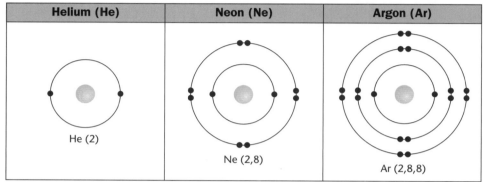

Fig. 5.4 Electronic configuration of helium, neon and argon.

All the noble gases, except helium, have eight electrons in the outer shell. Helium has two electrons in its outmost shell.

- Atoms of noble gases are stable and unreactive. They do **not** combine with other atoms to form compounds.
- Noble gases exist as individual atoms.

Scientists believe that the stability of a noble gas is due to its fully filled outer shell. It will not take in, or lose, any more electrons.

The atoms of other elements do not have full shells of electrons. That is why they are reactive. By reacting with each other, the atoms can lose, gain or share electrons until they have eight electrons in their outer shells and so become stable. Note that unlike the second and third shells, the maximum number of electrons in the first shell is two.

The formation of ions

An atom becomes an ion if it loses or gains electrons.

>
> **KEY POINT** An **ion** is a charged particle formed from an atom or a group of atoms by losing electrons or gaining electrons.

The table shows some examples of ions.

Name of element	Name of ion	Formula
sodium	sodium ion	Na^+
magnesium	magnesium ion	Mg^{2+}
aluminium	aluminium ion	Al^{3+}
chlorine	chloride ion	Cl^-
oxygen	oxide ion	O^{2-}
nitrogen	nitride ion	N^{3-}

- Metals form positively charged ions (**cations**) whereas non-metals form negatively charged ions (**anions**).
- Positively charged ions are formed by the loss of electrons.
- Negatively charge ions are formed by the gain of electrons.

5.2 Bonding

- Compounds are formed when atoms of two or more elements are chemically combined.
- Chemical bonding involves either transferring or sharing electrons in the highest occupied energy levels (shells) of atoms.
- The joining of atoms together is called bonding.
- **Ionic** bonds and **covalent** bonds are two different types of bond.
- An arrangement of particles together is called a structure.

Ionic (or electrovalent) bond: The transfer of electrons

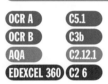

Sodium chloride

When sodium is heated and then placed in a gas jar of chlorine, the elements combine to form sodium chloride.

- The sodium atom loses its single valence (outer shell) electron to form a positively charged sodium ion. The sodium ion has the same electronic configuration as a stable neon atom:

$$Na \rightarrow Na^+ + e^-$$
$$(2,8,1) \rightarrow (2,8)^+$$

- The chlorine atom gains an electron to form a negatively charged chloride ion. The chloride ion has the same electronic configuration as a stable argon atom.

$$Cl + e^- \rightarrow Cl^-$$
$$(2,8,7) \quad (2,8,8)^-$$

- Positive sodium ions and negative chloride ions are attracted to one another by **electrostatic attraction** to form sodium chloride.

$$Na^+ + Cl^- \rightarrow Na^+ Cl^-$$

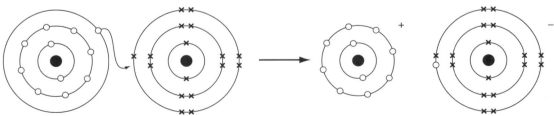

Fig. 5.5 Formation of ionic bond in sodium chloride.

- This is called a 'dot-and-cross' diagram. In a dot-and-cross diagram, the electrons of one atom are represented by dots, and crosses represent the electrons of another atom.
- Non-metallic ions obtain the stable octet configuration of a noble gas.
- The atom that loses electrons becomes a positive ion, the atom that receives electrons becomes a negative ion.

● The strong electrostatic attraction that holds the oppositely charged ions together is called **ionic bonding**. Compounds that contain ionic bonds are called **ionic compounds**.

Ionic bonding is sometimes called electrovalent bonding.

KEY POINT

The force of attraction that holds the sodium ions and chloride ions together is called ionic bonding.

Magnesium oxide

Magnesium burns in oxygen to form magnesium oxide.

● The magnesium atom loses two valence (outer shell) electrons to form a positively charged magnesium ion. The magnesium ion has the same electronic configuration as a stable neon atom:

$Mg \rightarrow Mg^{2+} + 2e^-$

$(2,8,2) \rightarrow (2,8)^{2+}$

● The oxygen atom gains two electrons to form a negatively charged oxide ion. The oxide ion has the same electronic configuration as a stable neon atom.

$O + 2e^- \rightarrow O^{2-}$

$(2,6) \qquad (2,8)^{2-}$

● Positive magnesium ions and negative oxide ions are attracted to one another by electrostatic attraction to form magnesium oxide (MgO).

$Mg^{2+} + O^{2-} \rightarrow Mg^{2+}O^{2-}$

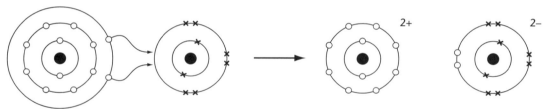

Fig. 5.6 Formation of ionic band in magnesium oxide.

Sodium oxide

Sodium rapidly tarnishes in air to form sodium oxide.

● Two sodium atoms each lose a valence (outer shell) electron to form two positively charged sodium ions. The sodium ion has the same electronic configuration as a stable neon atom:

$2Na \rightarrow 2Na^+ + 2e^-$

$2(2,8,1) \rightarrow 2(2,8)^{2+}$

● The oxygen atom gains the two electrons to form a negatively charged oxide ion. The oxide ion has the same electronic configuration as a stable neon atom.

$O + 2e^- \rightarrow O^{2-}$

$(2,6) \qquad (2,8)^{2-}$

● Positive sodium ions and negative oxide ions are attracted to one another by electrostatic attraction to form sodium oxide (Na_2O).

$2Na^+ + O^{2-} \rightarrow (Na^+)_2O^{2-}$

Magnesium chloride

Magnesium burns in chlorine to form magnesium chloride.

- The magnesium atom loses two valence (outer shell) electrons to form a positively charged magnesium ion. The magnesium ion has the same electronic configuration as a stable neon atom:

$Mg \rightarrow Mg^{2+} + 2e^-$

$(2,8,2) \rightarrow (2,8)^{2+}$

- Two chlorine atoms each gain an electron to form two negatively charged chloride ions. Each chloride ion has the same electronic configuration as a stable argon atom.

$2Cl + e^- \rightarrow 2Cl^-$

$2(2,8,7) \qquad 2(2,8,8)^-$

- Positive magnesium ions and negative chloride ions are attracted to one another by electrostatic attraction to form magnesium chloride ($MgCl_2$).

$Mg^{2+} + 2Cl^- \rightarrow Mg^{2+}(Cl^-)_2$

 Metals react with non-metals to form ionic compounds.

 The ions in an ionic compound have the electronic configuration of a noble gas.

Some metals form more than one type of ion. Iron forms Fe^{2+} and Fe^{3+} and copper forms Cu^+ and Cu^{2+}. The charge on the ion for these metals is shown in the name of the compounds formed. Iron(II) chloride means that it contains the Fe^{2+} ion. Iron(III) chloride means that it contains the Fe^{3+} ion.

Edexcel only.

Some ions are made up of groups of atoms. These ions are called **polyatomic ions**. Examples of polyatomic ions are the ammonium ion (NH_4^+), carbonate ion (CO_3^{2-}) and sulfate(VI) ion (SO_4^{2-}).

Formulae of compounds from their ions

The formula of a compound is a set of symbols and numbers. The symbols show the elements present in the compound. The numbers give the ratio in which the ions or atoms of different elements are present.

The formula of an ionic compound is found by balancing the charges on the positive ions with those on the negative ions.

 The total positive and negative charges must be equal in an ionic compound.

The sodium ion has a charge of +1 and the chloride ion a charge of –1. Adding the charges together, we find that (+1) + (–1) = 0. The formula of sodium chloride is NaCl.

The easiest way to balance the charges is:

- write down the ions with the charges $X^{m+} Y^{n-}$
- move the values m and n diagonally (but without the charges) $X^m \swarrow Y^n$
- formula is $X_n Y_m$

Potassium bromide

The ions are K^+ and Br^-, so its formula is:

$$K^{\textcircled{+}} \diagdown Br^{\textcircled{-}} \longrightarrow KBr$$

Aluminium oxide

The ions are Al^{3+} and O^{2-}, so its formula is Al_2O_3

$$Al^{\textcircled{3}+} \diagdown O^{\textcircled{2}-} \longrightarrow Al_2O_3$$

Magnesium carbonate

The ions are Mg^{2+} and CO_3^{2-}, so its formula is $MgCO_3$

Note the ratio 2:2 is the same as 1:1 so the '2s' cancel out.

Remember that the metal is always written first.

$$Mg^{\textcircled{2}+} \diagdown CO_3^{\textcircled{2}-} \longrightarrow Mg_2(CO_3)_2 \longrightarrow MgCO_3$$

Aluminium nitrate

The ions are Al^{3+} and NO_3^-, the formula is $Al(NO_3)_3$.

$$Al^{\textcircled{3}+} \diagdown NO_3^{\textcircled{1}-} \longrightarrow Al(NO_3)_3$$

- the subscripts are the simplest set of whole numbers, e.g. CaO and **not** Ca_2O_2
- the subscript '1' is not written, e.g. KCl and **not** K_1Cl_1
- polyatomic ions such as OH^-, CO_3^{2-} and SO_4^{2-} should be written within brackets, e.g. $Fe(OH)_2$ and **not** $FeOH_2$.

Properties of ionic compounds

Sodium chloride has the following properties:

- a high melting point
- it is soluble in water
- when solid, it does not conduct electricity
- it conducts electricity when molten
- aqueous solution conducts electricity.

Magnesium oxide has similar properties:

- a very high melting point
- when solid, it does not conduct electricity
- aqueous solution conducts electricity
- it conducts electricity when molten.

The above properties can be explained by their structures. The positive ions are electrostatically attracted to the negative ions. A sodium chloride crystal consists of a regular arrangement of equal numbers of sodium ions and chloride ions. This is called a **giant ionic lattice**.

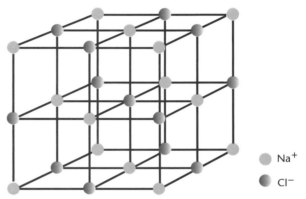

Na$^+$

Cl$^-$

Fig. 5.7 Sodium chloride lattice.

Magnesium oxide has a similar lattice.

Thus the above properties can be explained:

- strong attraction between positive and negative ions therefore they have high melting points
- ions cannot move in solid so do not conduct electricity
- ions can move in solution or in a molten liquid so conducts electricity.

Covalent bond

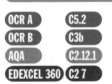

| KEY POINT | A covalent bond is formed by the sharing of a pair of electrons between two atoms. |

After bonding, each atom gets the electronic configuration of a noble gas.

When atoms combine by sharing electrons, molecules are formed.

| KEY POINT | A **molecule** is a group of atoms held together by covalent bonds. |

Chlorine molecule (Cl$_2$)

A chlorine atom has seven valence electrons. It needs one more electron to form a stable octet structure of eight electrons.

It can do this by sharing a pair of electrons through covalent bonding.

- The sharing of two electrons is called a **single bond**.
- It is represented by a single line 'Cl–Cl'.

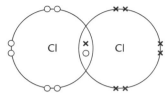

Fig. 5.8 Electron sharing in a chlorine molecule.

Oxygen

The electronic configuration of an oxygen atom is (2,6). Each oxygen atom has only six valence electrons, i.e. two electrons fewer than eight. Each oxygen atom shares two pairs of two electrons to form the covalent bond O_2

- The sharing of two pairs of electrons is called a **double bond**.
- It is represented by a double line O=O.

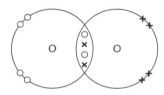

Fig. 5.9 Electron sharing in an oxygen molecule.

Molecules of compounds

A large number of compounds exist as covalent molecules. Covalent or molecular compounds are molecules made from two or more different atoms linked together by covalent bonding.

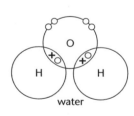
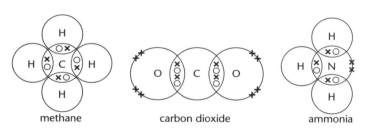

Fig. 5.10 Covalent compounds.

Water (H_2O), methane (CH_4), carbon dioxide (CO_2) and ammonia (NH_3) are examples of covalent compounds.

The 3-D models of these compounds are:

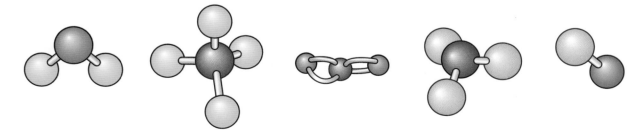

KEY POINT In a covalent molecule, each atom has the same electronic configuration as a noble gas.

KEY POINT Non-metals combine by sharing electrons to form covalent bonds.

Properties of covalent molecules

The structure of simple covalent molecules explains their properties. There are strong covalent bonds between atoms in a covalent molecule. However, between the molecules there are weak attractive forces.

Fig. 5.11 shows a two dimensional structure of iodine. Iodine, carbon dioxide and water:

Fig. 5.11 Iodine lattice showing arrangment of iodine molecules.

- have low melting points and boiling points because the forces between the molecules are weak. It is these intermolecular that are overcome, not the covalent bonds when the substance melts or boils.
- do not conduct electricity because there are no free electrons or an overall electric charge.

Carbon dioxide (a gas), water (a liquid) and iodine (a solid) are covalent substances.

Giant structures

AQA also refers to giant structures as macromolecules

Some covalent molecules have giant covalent structures. They can be made up of one type of atom (graphite and diamond) or of two or more atoms such as silicon(IV) oxide.

Giant molecular structures are made up of thousands of atoms held together by strong covalent bonds. They have high melting and boiling points because it takes a lot of energy to break the bonds. They do not conduct electricity because there are no ions or free electrons to carry the current.

They are insoluble in water and organic solvents, because the bonds are too strong to be broken by the solvents.

Diamond

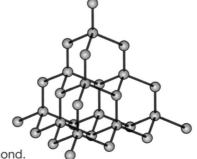

Fig. 5.12 Structure of diamond.

Diamond is made up of carbon atoms joined together by covalent bonds.

Diamond is:

- lustrous, colourless and clear (transparent)
- hard and has a high melting point; because a large amount of energy is needed to break the bonds
- insoluble in water
- does not conduct electricity when solid or molten because all the electrons are used up in the covalent bonds so there are no free electrons.

Diamond is used in:

- cutting tools because it is very hard and has a high melting point
- jewellery because it is lustrous and colourless.

Graphite

Graphite is made up of carbon. Each carbon atom is bonded covalently to three other atoms. The carbon atoms are arranged in layers. The 4th bond on each carbon atom is used to connect the layers (see dashed lines in Fig. 5.13). This bond is so long that the electrons in it are not bound to any atom but they are free to move through the structure.

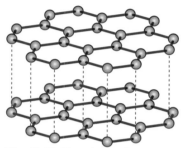

Fig. 5.13 Structure of graphite.

The movement of electrons means that graphite can conduct electricity but only in the plane between the layers.

Graphite is soft compared to diamond due to the weak forces between the layers. It has a high melting point because there are many strong covalent bonds to break.

Graphite is used in:

- pencil lead, as it is slippery and black because layers of carbon atoms are weakly held together and can slide easily over each other
- lubricants, because it is slippery
- electrolysis as an electrode as it conducts electricity because it has delocalised electrons that can move, and has a high melting point.

Nanomolecules

OCR B   C4g
AQA   C2.12.2
EDEXCEL 360   C2 7

Notice how the structure of this molecule is similar to a football and the biodomes at the Eden project. It consists of a mixture of 5-sided (pentagons) and 6-sided rings (hexagons)

C_{60} is the smallest molecule of a group called buckminsterfullerene (bucky balls). The diagram shows a molecule of C_{60}. Each carbon atom is attached to three other carbon atoms. Like graphite, it has free electrons so it can conduct electricity.

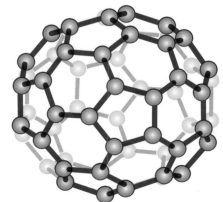

Fig. 5.15 Structure of buckminsterfullerene.

Fig. 5.16 Biodome at the Eden Project.

Buckminsterfullerenes, like graphite and diamond, are allotropes of carbon.

Buckminsterfullerene is:
- a black solid
- deep red in solution in petrol.

Fullerenes can be joined together to make nanotubes. Nanotubes:
- are very strong
- conduct electricity.

Nanotubes are used as:
- semiconductors in electrical circuits
- industrial catalysts (the catalysts are attached to the nanotube, giving the catalyst a large surface area)
- reinforcement graphite in tennis rackets.

Fullerenes are used to cage other molecules, e.g. in new drug delivery systems.

Nanoscience refers to molecules such as Buckminsterfullerenes that contain a few hundred atoms. The molecules are about 1 to 100 nanometres in size. Nanoparticles show different properties to the same materials in bulk and have a high surface area to volume ratio. This may lead to the development of new computers, new catalysts, new coatings, highly selective sensors and stronger and lighter construction materials.

Nanomolecules can be made either by:
- molecule-by-molecule building of a product, using positional chemistry
- or by starting with a bigger structure and then removing matter to produce nanoscale features.

The diagram shows a carbon nanotube (CNT).

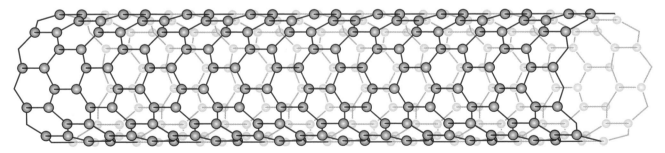

Fig. 5.16 A carbon nanotube (CNT).

Metallic bonding

OCR A   C5.4
OCR B   C3h
AQA   C2.12.1
EDEXCEL 360   C2 6

> The sea of electrons can move throughout the structure. This explains the high electrical conductivity of metals.

Metal atoms are held strongly to each other by **metallic bonding**. In the metal lattice, the atoms lose their outer valence electrons and become positively charged.

● The valence electrons no longer belong to any metal atom and are said to be **delocalised**.

The electrons move freely between the metal ions like a cloud of negative charge. A metal consists of a lattice structure of positive ions surrounded by a 'sea of mobile electrons'.

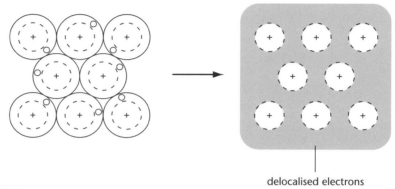

delocalised electrons

Fig. 5.17 The metallic bond.

Bonding, structure and properties

Bonding	Structure	Properties
ionic	**giant structure** e.g. sodium chloride magnesium oxide	**High melting point** Usually soluble in water but insoluble in organic solvents Conduct electricity when molten or when dissolved in water
covalent	**molecular** e.g. chlorine oxygen methane	Usually gases or low boiling point liquids Usually insoluble in water but soluble in organic solvents Do not conduct electricity
	giant structure e.g. silicon dioxide diamond	Solids High melting points. Insoluble in water and organic solvents Do not conduct electricity
	nanomolecules e.g. Buckminster fullerenes	Solids High melting point Insoluble in water but soluble in organic solvents Conduct electricity
metallic	**giant structure** e.g. copper, sodium, magnesium	Solids High densities Good electrical conductors

Note: If a substance conducts electricity when solid and when molten, it must be a **metal**.

HOW SCIENCE WORKS

OCR A	C5.4
OCR B	C3f
AQA	C2.12.1
EDEXCEL 360	C2 6

'Metallic' hydrogen

Hydrogen has one electron in its outer shell. It is a colourless gas and an electrical insulator. The other elements that contain one electron in their outer shell are the Group 1 metals (lithium, sodium, potassium, rubidium, caesium and francium). These are solids that are good conductors of electricity. Scientists predicted that it would be possible to make 'metallic' hydrogen at pressures two million times that of atmospheric pressure. (This is approximately the pressure at the centre of the Earth.)

Scientists have achieved these pressures producing hydrogen that is opaque (light cannot pass through it). This indicates that the electron configuration of hydrogen has changed. In fact it has become a superconductor.

A superconductor is a substance that will conduct electricity without resistance below a certain temperature. The first superconductor was discovered by Nobel prize winner Heike-Kamerlingh Onnes. He found that when he cooled mercury to −269°C it lost all resistance.

It is believed that the planets Jupiter and Saturn are mainly composed of hot metallic hydrogen. Metallic hydrogen consists of a crystal lattice made up of protons. The electrons are free to move and behave like the 'sea of electrons' in metals. It is thought that the intense magnetic field of Jupiter is caused by electrical currents in the liquid metallic hydrogen that is spinning rapidly in the core of the planet.

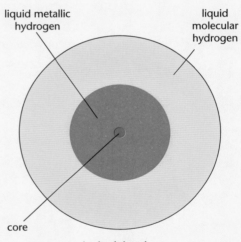

Jupiter's interior

Metallic hydrogen could be used as a fuel. It would give off vast amounts of energy when changing back to hydrogen gas. When metallic hydrogen is burned, it gives off far more energy than the standard liquid hydrogen/liquid oxygen fuel used in Space shuttles.

Scientists have put forward the theory that metallic hydrogen may be a superconductor at temperatures as high as room temperature (290 K), far higher than any other known candidate material.

The benefits of superconductors include:
- loss-free power transmission
- super-fast electronic circuits
- powerful electromagnets.

As soon as a current begins flowing in a closed loop of a superconductor, it will flow forever.

Superconductors are used in magnetic-levitation (MagLev). Trains such as that used on the Yamanashi MagLev Test line in Japan can be made to 'float' on strong

HOW SCIENCE WORKS

superconducting magnets. There is hardly any friction between the train and its tracks. The trains can reach speeds of 580 kilometres per hour. However, further research has been limited because of fears that the strong magnetic fields can create a bio-hazard. Unfortunately, the MAGLEV train, a shuttle at Birmingham International Airport was shut down in 1997 because it was unreliable.

At present the drawbacks of superconductors are that:

- they only work at very low temperatures
- there is a need to develop superconductors that will work at 20 °C.

Metallic hydrogen may be the answer.

HOW SCIENCE WORKS
Questions

1. The density of Jupiter is larger than would be expected if it was made up of only metallic hydrogen. Scientists have predicted that the core of Jupiter also contains metallic deuterium and metallic tritium. Deuterium and tritium are isotopes of hydrogen.
   Hydrogen, deuterium and tritium have a different:
   A atomic number
   B number of electron shells (energy levels)
   C number of electrons
   D number of neutrons [1]
2. Draw and label a diagram showing all the particles present in an atom of deuterium. [2]
3. Why did scientists think that metallic hydrogen would conduct electricity? [1]
4. Describe how metals such as lithium and sodium conduct electricity. [4]
5. Draw a diagram to illustrate the structure of metallic hydrogen.
   Mercury melts at −39°C and boils at 359°C. [2]
6. What is the physical state of mercury at:
   (a) 20°C
   (b) −269°C? [2]
7. Why does the fact that metallic hydrogen is opaque indicate that the structure of hydrogen has changed? [1]
8. A biohazard is defined as a hazard to humans or the environment resulting from biological agents or conditions.
   State with reasons whether superconductors are biohazards. [4]

Exam practice questions

1. What is the total number of electrons in a water molecule?

   A   6   C   10

   B   8   D   12   [1]

2. The melting point and boiling points of the hydrides of elements in group 4 are given in the table.

Hydride	Melting point °C	Boiling point °C
CH_4	–182	–161
GeH_4	–165	–88
SiH_4	–185	–112
SnH_4	–150	–52

   Which hydride remains a gas over the widest temperature range?

   A CH_4 C SiH_4

   B GeH_4 D SnH_4 [1]

3. The number of valence electrons for the elements hydrogen to magnesium was plotted against proton number of the element. Which graph was obtained?

   A 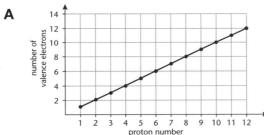   B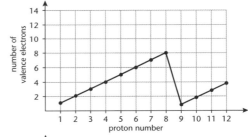

   C 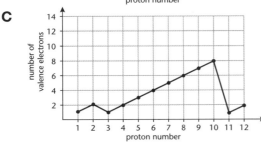   D 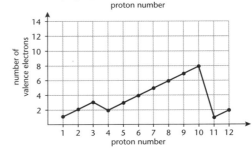   [1]

4. Choose words from the list below to fill in the gaps in the passage. A word may be used once, more than once or not at all.

   electrons   isotopes   protons   neutrons   nucleus   shells

   Atoms are made up of three different particles ____1____ which are positively charged; ____2____ which have no charge and ____3____ which are negatively charged. The negatively charge particles are arranged in ____4____ around the ____5____. The particles with a negligible mass are ____6____.

   All atoms of the same element contain the same number of ____7____ and ____8____. Atoms of the same element with a different number of ____9____ are known as ____10____.   [10]

Exam practice questions

5. Complete the table below by stating the type of:

(i) elements present in the compound

(ii) bonding in the compound

The first one has been completed for you.

Compound	Type of	
	element	bonding
sodium chloride (NaCl)	sodium metal → → ionic chlorine non-metal →	ionic
ammonia (NH₃)		
methane (CH₄)		
calcium oxide		
magnesium phosphide		

[4]

6. Match each of the following substances to their type of structure.

Type of structure
atoms only
giant ionic compound
giant molecular structure
giant structure of atoms
metallic structure
nanomolecule
simple molecular structure

Substance
Buckminster fullerene
copper
graphite
helium
magnesium oxide
silicon dioxide
sulfur

[4]

7. (a) Complete the magnesium oxide lattice by adding:

⬤ for an oxide ion and

⬤ for a magnesium ion.

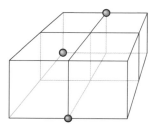

[3]

(b) Complete the diamond structure by adding lines to show the bonds between the carbon atoms.

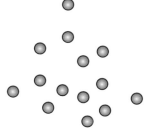

[3]

Exam practice questions

8. Ozone is a very pale blue gas. It is formed in the stratosphere by the action of high-energy radiation on oxygen. It has the formula O_3. (The relative molecular mass of any gas has the same volume at the same temperature and pressure.)

Are the following statements true or false? Explain your answers.

(a) Oxygen and ozone are both coloured gases. [1]

(b) Ozone is an isotope of oxygen. [1]

(c) Ozone is denser than oxygen. [2]

(d) If one oxygen molecule has 16 electrons and 16 neutrons then one ozone molecule should have 24 protons, 24 electrons and 24 neutrons. [2]

9. When the elements are arranged in order of their increasing atomic masses, the order is almost the same as if the atoms had been arranged in the order of the number of protons in the nucleus. The table below shows the positions of the first 20 elements in the periodic table.

1 **H** Hydrogen 1							4 **He** Helium 2
7 **Li** Lithium 3	9 **Be** Berylium 4	11 **B** Boron 5	12 **C** Carbon 6	14 **N** Nitrogen 7	16 **O** Oxygen 8	19 **F** Fluorine 9	20 **Ne** Neon 10
23 **Na** Sodium 11	24 **Mg** Magnesium 12	27 **Al** Aluminium 13	28 **Si** Silicon 14	31 **P** Phosphorus 15	32 **S** Sulfur 16	35.5 **Cl** Chlorine 17	40 **Ar** Argon 18
39 **K** Potassium 19	40 **Ca** Calcium 20						

(a) Suggest, with reasons, (i) the atomic number and (ii) the atomic mass of silicon. [2]

(b) **(i)** Element X has 1 less proton than Y but 2 more neutrons. Identify X and Y from the above table.

(ii) Element T has 2 more protons than S but 2 less neutrons. Identify S and T. [2]

(c) Why would you expect the mass number of an element to be a whole number? Naturally occurring neon has an average atomic mass of 20.2. Neon has two isotopes with atomic masses of 20 and 22. [2]

(d) **(i)** What is the ratio of Ne-20 to Ne-22 in naturally occurring neon?

(ii) Which other element in the table above MUST have isotopes? [2]

The periodic table

The following topics are covered in this chapter:

- **The periodic table**
- **Carbon compounds**
- **Common organic compounds**
- **The four spheres of the Earth**

6.1 The periodic table

Periods and groups

OCR A   4.1
OCR B   3c
AQA   12.1
EDEXCEL 360   1A 5

In the periodic table, the elements are arranged in order of increasing proton (atomic) number. Elements with similar properties are placed in the same vertical group.

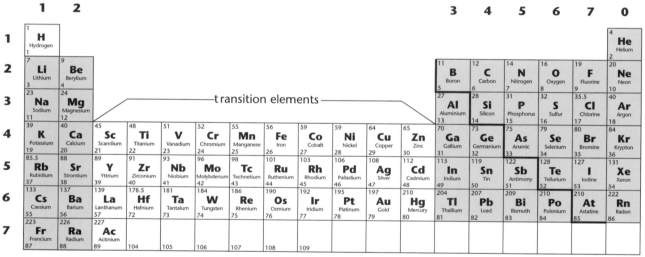

Fig. 6.1 The periodic table.

There are:

- seven horizontal rows of elements called **periods**
- eight vertical columns of elements called **groups**. The elements in a group have similar properties
- the main block of elements are shaded
- the elements between the two parts of the main block are the **transition metals**
- the bold stepped line of the table divides metals on the left-hand side from non-metals on the right-hand side.

Arrangement of electrons and the periodic table

Elements in the same group in the periodic table have the same number of electrons in the highest energy levels (outer electrons). Fig. 6.1 shows the arrangement of the electrons and how they fit into the table.

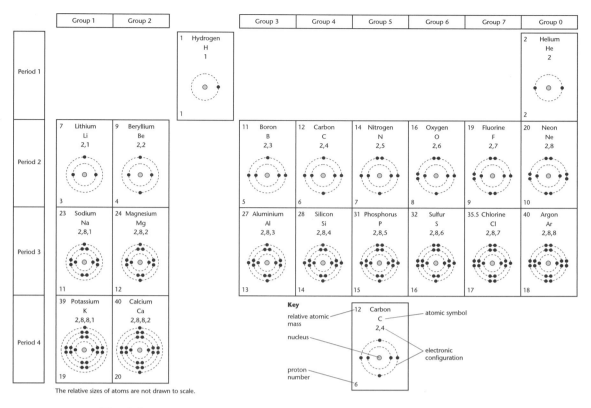

The relative sizes of atoms are not drawn to scale.

Fig. 6.2 The electronic configuration of the first 20 elements.

Property	Example
The periodic table can be used to identify:	
• the atomic number of an element	The element, phosphorus (P) has atomic number of 15
• the name or symbol of an element given its atomic number	The element with an atomic number of 12 is magnesium, Mg
• the elements in a compound from its formula	The compound $CaSiO_3$ contains calcium, silicon and oxygen
• elements that are in the same group	Elements in the same group have the same number of electrons in their outermost shell: Group 1 elements have 1 electron in the outer shell Group 7 electrons have 7 electrons in the outer shell Group 0 electrons have 8 electrons in the outer shell
• elements that are in the same period	All the elements in period 3 have three occupied shells in the electronic structure, e.g. aluminium (Al) 2,8,3; silicon (Si) 2,8,4 and chlorine (Cl) 2,8,7 are all in the same period
• the electronic structure of the first 20 elements in the periodic table	Sulfur is in group 6 period 3, it therefore has 6 electrons in its outermost shell and 3 occupied shells. Its structure therefore, is 2,8,6
• the relative atomic mass of an element	The relative atomic mass of chlorine is 35.5

Hazard symbols

OCR A   C4.1

> You should treat all chemicals with care, and do not taste them unless you are given permission by your teacher to do so.

You must be able to recognise and explain the significance of hazard symbols. You will find them in the laboratory on bottles, in worksheets and in text books.

Hazard sign	Meaning
	Corrosive These substances attack and destroy living things so do not get them on your skin or in your eyes
	Oxidising These substances help other substances to burn more easily
	Toxic (poisonous) These substances can cause death if they are either swallowed, breathed in or absorbed through the skin
	If this symbol contains a small 'h' it is **Harmful** but not as dangerous as substances that are toxic If this symbol contains an 'i' it is an **Irritant**. They are not as harmful as corrosive substances, but they can cause the skin to go red and/or blister
	Highly flammable These substances easily catch fire They must be kept away from naked flames

Properties and reaction of group 1 elements (alkali metals)

OCR A   C4.1
OCR B   C3d
AQA   15.4

The first three elements in group 1 are lithium (Li), sodium (Na) and potassium (K). Because lithium, sodium and potassium belong to the same group in the periodic table, they must have very similar physical and chemical properties.

Element	Symbol	Appearance	Melting point in °C	Boiling point in °C	Density in g/cm³
lithium	Li	soft, grey metal	181	1330	0.54
sodium	Na	soft, light grey metal	98	890	0.97
potassium	K	very soft, blue/grey metal	63	774	0.86

Physical properties
- The alkali metals have low melting points, low boiling points and low densities compared to other metals.
- They are soft metals that can be easily cut with a knife. The cut surfaces are shiny, but rapidly tarnish as the metals react with oxygen in the air (see below).
- The melting points and boiling points of the alkali metals decrease on going down the group.
- They are good conductors of electricity.
- Their compounds are ionic and soluble in water.

Flame test

The alkali metals can be recognised by the colours they produce in a flame test. To perform a flame test:

- The tip of a nichrome wire is placed in concentrated hydrochloric acid.
- The tip of the nichrome wire is placed in a roaring Bunsen flame until there is a constant orange/yellow colour.
- The tip of the nichrome wire is dipped into the chloride of the alkali metal.
- The tip of the nichrome wire is again placed in the flame and the colour observed.

lithium	→	crimson	potassium →	lilac
sodium	→	yellow	rubidium →	red

The study of spectra has helped chemists to discover and identify new elements.

Helium was first discovered in the Sun in 1868 using the technique of spectroscopy. Helium is named after the Greek word for Sun *helios*.

Chemical properties

Alkali metals have similar properties because when they react, an atom loses one electron to form a positive ion with a stable electronic structure.

$$M \rightarrow M^+ + e$$

M represents an alkali metal.

This is an example of oxidation since oxidation is a loss of electrons.

It becomes easier for an alkali metal to lose its outmost electron on going down the group. As the electrons get further away from the nucleus, the attraction between the nucleus and the electron gets smaller. The reduction in attraction explains why the alkali metals get more reactive going down the group.

- Lithium, sodium and potassium are very reactive metals.
- They are stored under oil to prevent them from reacting with air and water.
- The metals get more reactive going down the group.

Reaction with water

They are called **alkali metals** because they react with water to form alkaline solutions.

lithium	+	water	→	lithium hydroxide	+ hydrogen
$2Li$	+	$2H_2O$	→	$2LiOH$	+ H_2

sodium	+	water	→	sodium hydroxide	+ hydrogen
$2Na$	+	$2H_2O$	→	$2NaOH$	+ H_2

potassium	+	water	→	potassium hydroxide	+ hydrogen
$2K$	+	$2H_2O$	→	$2KOH$	+ H_2

Reaction with oxygen

They burn in air or oxygen to form basic oxides $((M^+)_2O^{2-})$.

e.g. lithium + oxygen → lithium oxide

$$4Li + O_2 \rightarrow 2Li_2O$$

Caesium burns with a sky blue colour.

Each alkali burns with a characteristic flame colour (see flame test above).

The oxides dissolve in water to form alkalis (M^+OH^-)

e.g. sodium oxide + water → sodium hydroxide
Na_2O + H_2O → $2NaOH$

Reaction with chlorine

They burn in chlorine to form a white crystalline solid of the metal chloride (M^+Cl^-).

potassium + chlorine → potassium chloride
$2K$ + Cl_2 → $2KCl$

> **KEY POINT**
> These metals are in the same group of the periodic table because their reactions are very similar.

You should be able to predict the properties of rubidium, knowing the properties of lithium, sodium and potassium.

The next three members of group 1 are rubidium (Rb), caesium (Cs) and francium (Fr). Francium is the most reactive metal.

Properties and reaction of group 7 elements (the halogens)

OCR A — C4.1
OCR B — C3e
AQA — 2.12.1

Remember diatomic means two atoms per molecule e.g.Cl_2

The first four elements in group 7 are fluorine (F), chlorine (Cl), bromine (Br) and iodine (I). They exist as diatomic molecules. Because fluorine, chlorine, bromine and iodine belong to the same group in the periodic table, they must have very similar chemical properties.

- Chlorine, bromine and iodine are poisonous.
- Bromine and iodine are corrosive.

Physical properties

They have different physical properties.

Element	Symbol	Appearance	Melting point in °C
fluorine	F	pale yellow gas	−220
chlorine	Cl	yellow/green gas	−101
bromine	Br	red/brown volatile liquid	−7
iodine	I	dark grey crystalline solid, purple vapour when heated	114

- The halogens have low melting points and low boiling points.
- The melting points and boiling points of the halogens increase going down the group.
- They are poor conductors of electricity.
- They are soluble in water and they react with water (see below).
- They are soluble in organic solvents such as hexane to form solutions with characteristic colours:
  chlorine – colourless; bromine – orange; iodine – purple

Iodine exists as 'free' diatomic molecules in the vapour state and in organic solvents; hence it has the same purple colour.

Chemical properties

Halogens have similar properties because when they react, an atom gains one electron to form a negative ion with a stable electronic structure.

$+ e \rightarrow X^-$

X represents a halogen.

This is an example of reduction since reduction is a gain of electrons.

It becomes less easy for a halogen to gain an electron on going down the group. This is because the attraction between the nucleus and the electron gets smaller. The reduction in attraction explains why the halogens get less reactive going down the group.
- Fluorine, chlorine, bromine and iodine are reactive non-metals.
- The non-metals get less reactive going down the group.
- Fluorine is the most reactive non-metal.

Reaction with water

When they are added to water, a mixture of acids is formed. The acid containing oxygen is a bleaching agent.

e.g. chlorine + water $\rightarrow$ hydrochloric acid + chloric(I) acid
$$Cl_2 + H_2O \rightarrow HCl + HOCl$$

The test for chlorine gas is that it turns blue litmus red and then bleaches the litmus.

Reaction with metals

The halogens react vigorously with metals to form salts (halides). The name **halogen** means '**salt producer**'.

- **chlorine** produces **chlorides**
  e.g. iron + chlorine $\rightarrow$ iron(III) chloride
  $$2Fe + 3Cl_2 \rightarrow 2FeCl_3$$

- **bromine** produces **bromides**
  e.g. magnesium + bromine $\rightarrow$ magnesium bromide
  $$Mg + Br_2 \rightarrow MgBr_2$$

- **iodine** produces **iodides**
  e.g. sodium + iodine $\rightarrow$ sodium iodide
  $$2Na + I_2 \rightarrow 2NaI(s)$$

Nearly all the metal chlorides are ionic solids. All metal chlorides are soluble in water except silver chloride and lead(II) chloride.

Displacement reactions of the halogens

KEY POINT **A more reactive halogen will displace a less reactive halogen from one of its compounds.**

When chlorine is bubbled into an aqueous solution of potassium bromide, chlorine displaces the bromine. The colourless solution turns orange.

chlorine	+ potassium bromide	→ bromine	+ potassium chloride
Cl_2	+ 2KBr	→ Br_2	+ 2KCl

Similarly chlorine	+ potassium iodide	→ iodine	+ potassium chloride
Cl_2	+ 2KI	→ I_2	+ 2KCl

bromine	+ potassium iodide	→ iodine	+ potassium bromide
Br_2	+ 2KI	→ I_2	+ 2KBr

But when iodine is added to potassium chloride or potassium bromide there is no reaction.

There is also **no** reaction when bromine is added to potassium chloride.

Uses

Chlorine is used to:
- bleach dyes
- kill bacteria in water (sterilise)
- make pesticides and plastics.

Iodine is used to:
- sterilise wounds.

Sodium chloride is used:
- as a preservative
- as a flavouring
- to manufacture chlorine.

Transition metals

OCR B   C3g

> **KEY POINT** Transition metals are in a block of metals between group 2 and group 3 in the periodic table. The first series of transition metals occurs in period 4.

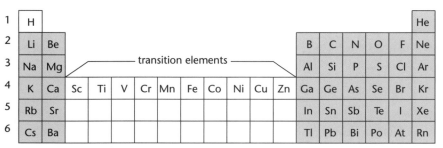

Vanadium (V), chromium (Cr), manganese (Mn), iron (Fe), nickel (Ni) and copper (Cu) are examples of transition metals. They are all metals and they have typical metallic properties:

Fig. 6.3 The position of the transition metals in the periodic table.

- high melting points, high boiling points and high densities
- a shiny appearance
- good conductors of heat and electricity
- some transition metals are magnetic, e.g. iron and nickel.

Transition metals have some special properties because a lower energy level (inner shell) is filled in the atoms of the elements between groups 2 and 3. The third energy level can hold up to 18 electrons. The third energy level is filled after two electrons have occupied the fourth energy level.

One such special property is that these metals can show more than one oxidation state, e.g. iron can exist as Fe^{2+} and Fe^{3+}. They all form ions with a charge of +2.

Another special property of the compounds of transition elements is that they are often coloured:
- copper compounds are blue
- iron(II) compounds are light green
- iron(III) compounds are orange/brown.

Transition metal compounds are therefore used in dyes and pigments.

Transition elements and their compounds are often catalysts:
- iron in the Haber process
- nickel in the manufacture of margarine
- vanadium(V) oxide in the manufacture of sulfuric acid.

KEY POINT Thermal decomposition is a reaction in which a substance is broken down into at least two other substances by heat.

The test for carbon dioxide is that it turns limewater milky.

Transition metal carbonates such as $FeCO_3$, $CuCO_3$, $MnCO_3$ and $ZnCO_3$ undergo thermal decomposition to give the metal oxide and carbon dioxide.

During this reaction there is a colour change.
iron(II) carbonate $\rightarrow$ iron(II) oxide + carbon dioxide
$FeCO_3$ $\rightarrow$ FeO + CO_2

copper(II) carbonate $\rightarrow$ copper(II) oxide + carbon dioxide
$CuCO_3$ $\rightarrow$ CuO + CO_2

manganese(II) carbonate $\rightarrow$ manganese(II) oxide + carbon dioxide
$MnCO_3$ $\rightarrow$ MnO + CO_2

zinc carbonate $\rightarrow$ zinc oxide + carbon dioxide
$ZnCO_3$ $\rightarrow$ ZnO + CO_2

KEY POINT Precipitation is a reaction between solutions that makes an insoluble solid.

Sodium hydroxide solution is used to identify the presence of transition metal ions in solution. The metal hydroxides are precipitated and have characteristic colours.

copper(II) + sodium $\rightarrow$ copper(II) hydroxide + sodium
sulfate hydroxide (blue solid) sulfate
$CuSO_4$ + $2NaOH$ $\rightarrow$ $Cu(OH)_2$ + Na_2SO_4

Ionic equations

Many substances, especially ionic compounds, are soluble in water.

> **KEY POINT**
> An ionic equation is a simplified chemical equation that shows the reactions of ionic substances in water.

The above equation could be written as:

$$Cu^{2+} + SO_4^{2-} + 2Na^+ + 2OH^- \rightarrow Cu(OH)_2 + 2Na^+ + SO_4^{2-}$$

Since an equation represents change, anything which appears on both sides of the equation can be removed. The simplest equation is:

In this reaction, the spectator ions are $Na^+(aq)$ and $SO_4^{2-}(aq)$.

$$Cu^{2+} + 2OH^- \rightarrow Cu(OH)_2 \qquad \textit{ionic equation}$$

> **KEY POINT**
> The ions that are removed are called the 'spectator ions'.

Other precipitation reactions are:

iron(II) ions + hydroxide ions → iron(II) hydroxide (grey/green solid)

Fe^{2+} + $2OH^-$ → $Fe(OH)_2$

iron(III) ions + hydroxide ions → iron(III) hydroxide (orange/brown solid)

Fe^{3+} + $3OH^-$ → $Fe(OH)_3$

> **KEY POINT**
> All reactions involving soluble ionic compounds can be written as ionic equations, e.g. the reactions of halogens with metal halides of less reactive metals can be written this way:
>
> chlorine + potassium bromide → bromine + potassium chloride
>
> Cl_2 + $2KBr$ → Br_2 + $2KBr$
>
> Cl_2 + $2Br^-$ → Br_2 + $2Cl^-$

Half-equations

 AQA   C12.6
EDEXCEL 360   C2.6

The equations:

$Cu^{2+} + 2e^- \rightarrow Cu$

and $Cu - 2e^- \rightarrow Cu^{2+}$

are called half-equations.

> **KEY POINT**
> A half-equation is used to describe an oxidation or reduction half-reaction.

Oxidation and reduction can be remembered by OIL RIG (Oxidation Is Loss Reduction Is the Gain of electrons).

> **KEY POINT**
> Oxidation is the loss of electrons and reduction is the gain of electrons.

Half-equations are used to identify and represent redox reactions.

The atoms and charges must be balanced. Electrons are used to balance the charges. They can be added or subtracted from either side of the equation.

Half-equations can be combined to give the overall reaction or left as individual equations to show the oxidation reaction or the reduction reaction.

| word equation | zinc + hydrochloric acid → zinc chloride + hydrogen |

molecular equation $Zn + 2HCl \rightarrow ZnCl_2 + H_2$

ionic equation $Zn + 2H^+ \rightarrow Zn^{2+} + H_2$

Oxidation half-equation $Zn - 2e^- \rightarrow Zn^{2+}$

Electrons have been lost by zinc (reduction)

Reduction half-equation $2H^+ + 2e^- \rightarrow H_2$

Electrons have been gained by the H^+ (oxidation)

Half-equations are used to write the equations that occur at the anode and cathode during electrolysis:

In the electrolysis of dilute sulfuric acid

A at the anode: $2H^+ + 2e^- \rightarrow H_2$ (oxidation)

B at the cathode $4OH^- - 4e^- \rightarrow 2H_2O + O_2$ (reduction)

The overall equation is obtained by multiplying equation A by 2 and adding the two reactions:
$4H^+ + 4OH^- \rightarrow 2H_2 + 2H_2O + O_2$
but $4H^+ + 4OH^- \rightarrow 4H_2O$

so the overall equation is:
$2H_2O \rightarrow 2H_2 + O_2$

6.2 Carbon compounds

Alkane, alkenes and polymers

EDEXCEL 360 C2.5

Remember the names of alkanes end in –ane. The prefix tells you the number of carbon atoms. Pentane contains 5 carbon atoms.

Organic chemistry is 'the branch of chemistry concerned with compounds of carbon' such as methane (CH_4), ethene (C_2H_4), ethanol (C_2H_5OH), ethanoic acid (CH_3COOH) and ethyl ethanoate ($CH_3COOC_2H_5$).

Alkanes are saturated hydrocarbons. They contain only single carbon-carbon **covalent** bonds.

Name	Formula	Structure	State at room temp	Melting point	Boiling point
methane	CH_4	H–C–H (with H above and below)	gas	Increases down the family	Increases down the family
ethane	C_2H_6	H–C–C–H	gas		
propane	C_3H_8	H–C–C–C–H	gas		
butane	C_4H_{10}	H–C–C–C–C–H	gas		
pentane	C_5H_{12}	H–C–C–C–C–C–H	liquid		

Alkanes:

● have a general formula C_nH_{2n+2}. Thus $C_{20}H_{42}$ is an alkane
● have very few reactions apart from burning in air or oxygen.

Burning alkanes

When alkanes burn in **excess** air or oxygen, **carbon dioxide** and **water vapour** are formed.

methane + oxygen → carbon dioxide + water

$$CH_4 + 2O_2 \rightarrow CO_2 + 2H_2O$$

When alkanes burn in **limited** air, **carbon monoxide** and **water vapour** are formed.

methane + oxygen → carbon monoxide + water

$$2CH_4 + 3O_2 \rightarrow 2CO + 4H_2O$$

Carbon monoxide is very poisonous.

> All homes that burn gas should be well ventilated and have a carbon monoxide detector. Carbon monoxide has no smell.

Alkenes

Alkenes are **unsaturated** hydrocarbon molecules. They contain carbon–carbon **double** bonds.

Name	Formula	Structure	State at room temp	Melting point	Boiling point
ethene	C_2H_4	$C=C$ (with two H on each carbon)	gas	Increases down the family	Increases down the family
propene	C_3H_6	$C=C$ with CH_3 group	gas		

Alkenes:
- have a general formula C_nH_{2n}. Thus $C_{20}H_{40}$ is an alkene
- are much more reactive than alkanes.

Reactions of alkenes

- they burn in excess air or oxygen to form carbon dioxide and water vapour.

$$C_2H_4 + 3O_2 \rightarrow 2CO_2 + 2H_2O$$

- when they are bubbled through a solution of bromine, the solution changes from red-brown to colourless:

$$C_3H_6 + Br_2 \rightarrow C_3H_6Br_2$$

This is an addition reaction.

> **You must state the exact colour change. It is wrong to say that the solution turns clear. All solutions are clear.**

> **KEY POINT** An addition reaction is a reaction in which two or more molecules combine to form a single product.

Other addition reactions:
- they react with steam at high temperatures and high pressures in the presence of a catalyst to form alcohols

ethene + steam → ethanol

$$C_2H_4 \quad + \quad H_2O \quad \rightarrow \quad C_2H_5OH$$

This reaction is used to manufacture ethanol.

Some vegetable oils, such as olive oil and peanut oil, contain only one double bond. They are said to be monounsaturated.

Some vegetable oils, such as sunflower oil and safflower oil, contain many double bonds. They are said to be polyunsaturated.

When passed with hydrogen over a nickel catalyst at 200°C, alkanes are formed.

alkene + hydrogen →   alkane

$$C_nH_2n \quad + \quad H_2 \quad \rightarrow \quad C_nH_{2n+2}$$

This type of reaction is used to make margarine from vegetable oils. Vegetable oils are highly unsaturated liquids. By reacting with hydrogen, the unsaturated oils form saturated oils which are solids.

It is thought that eventually the Earth's supply of fossil fuels will run out. To slow down this process, oil reserves should be preserved and alternatives to oil developed. For example, alternative fuels to petrol and diesel should be developed so that oil can be used to make essential chemicals and medicines.

6.3 Common organic compounds

Polymers

EDEXCEL 360 **C2.5**

Alkenes can be used to make polymers such as poly(ethene) and poly(propene). In these reactions, many small molecules (monomers) join together to form very large molecules (polymers).

KEY POINT The process of joining together a large number of small molecules (monomers) to form a large molecule (polymer) is called polymerisation).

Notice that the monomer contains a double bond and this becomes a single bond when the molecules join together. The chains can have thousands of units added together. The properties of a sample of polymer depend upon chain length.

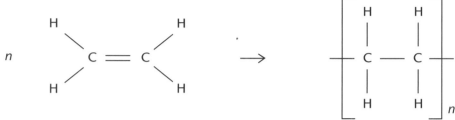

Fig. 6.4 Polymerisation of ethene to polyethene.

You should be able to work out that the name of the monomer from which poly(ethenol) is made is ethenol.

In this reaction, the monomer is ethene and the polymer poly(ethene) commonly known as polythene.

Polymers have properties that depend upon what they are made from and the conditions under which they are made. You may have made slime with different viscosities from the polymer poly(ethenol). The viscosity depends on how the polymers molecules are cross linked. The more linkages there are, the greater will be the viscosity.

Addition polymers such as poly(ethene) and poly(vinyl chloride) (PVC) have many uses.

They have replaced traditional materials such as metals, paper, cardboard and rubber. The table lists common polymers and their uses.

Polymer (alternative name, if any)	Monomer (alternative name, if any)	Uses
poly(ethene) (polythene)	ethene	cling film, plastic bags, coating for electric wire
poly(propene) (PP)	propene	food packaging, car parts
poly(chloroethene) poly(vinyl chloride) (PVC)	chloroethene (vinyl chloride)	plastic raincoats, shower curtains, insulation for electrical wiring
poly(styrene)	styrene	disposable cups, packaging, egg boxes, CD 'jewel' case
poly(tetrafluoroethene) (Teflon)	tetrafluoroethene	coating non-stick pans, making Gore-Tex
poly(methyl methacrylate) (Perspex)	methyl methacrylate	windscreens, aircraft windows, protective glass in hockey stadiums and large aquariums

Make sure that you can name the polymer from monomers and the monomer from polymers.

Polymers have many useful applications. New uses are being developed, for example, new packaging materials, waterproof coatings for fabrics, dental polymers, wound dressings, hydrogels and smart materials, including shape memory polymers.

Many polymers are non-biodegradable, so they are not broken down by micro-organisms, This can lead to problems with waste disposal.

Addition polymers are thermoplastics. This means that they melt when heated and they can then be remoulded into different shapes. Thermosetting plastics (e.g. Bakelite) do not melt on heating, instead they decompose. Many plastics are non-biodegradable.

Disposal of plastics

- Recycle – when you dispose of your rubbish you may be asked to separate your recyclable plastic from non-recyclable plastics.
- Burn in a plentiful supply of air. Plastics made up of carbon and hydrogen burn to give carbon dioxide and water. The heat energy can be used to supply power to factories. Plastics, such as Teflon and PVC give off poisonous gases when they are burnt, causing air pollution.
- Landfill – this gets the plastics out of sight, but, since they do not rot away, they cause land pollution.

6.4 The four spheres of the Earth

Lithosphere, biosphere, atmosphere and hydrosphere

The names of the four spheres are derived from the Greek words for air (atmo), life (bio), water (hydro), and stone (litho).

The Earth can be thought of as four inter-connected spheres:

- the lithosphere
- the hydrosphere
- the biosphere
- the atmosphere.

Life and material on the surface of the Earth can be classified in any of these spheres.

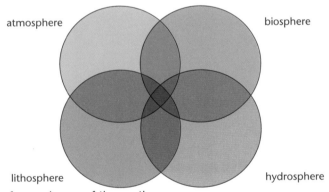

Fig. 6.5 The four spheres of the earth.

Sometimes all four spheres can be present in a single place. Soil has mineral material from the lithosphere; water of the hydrosphere present as moisture; insects and plants from the biosphere and air from the atmosphere.

Lithosphere

OCR A **C5.1**

The Earth's lithosphere is made up of tectonic plates. The outer layer of Earth is made up of the crust and the mantle. It is made up of a mixture of minerals.

The most abundant elements in the Earth's crust are:

oxygen (O)	47%
silicon (Si)	28%
aluminium (Al)	8%

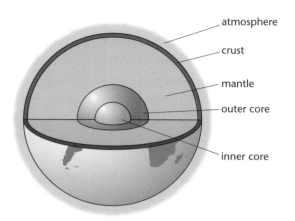

Fig. 6.6 The Earth's lithosphere.

> SiO$_2$ has a structure similar to diamond.

The commonest crystalline form of silicon dioxide is quartz. It is the main constituent of sandstone.

Over 95% of rocks in the Earth's crust are made up of silicates and aluminosilicates.

Minerals are naturally occurring chemicals. They can be elements or compounds. Some minerals are valuable gemstones because of their rarity, hardness and appearance.

A gemstone may be:
- a pure chemical element, e.g. silver, gold, carbon (diamond is essentially pure carbon)
- a relatively simple chemical compound, e.g. as quartz (silicon dioxide) or ruby (aluminium oxide)
- a more complex mixture of various compounds and elements, e.g. the garnet family includes a highly variable mix of iron, magnesium, aluminium, and calcium.

> The Earth is a sphere which is very slightly flattened at the poles.

It was once thought that the features of the Earth's surface were the result of the shrinking of the crust as the Earth cooled down following its formation.

Biosphere

Living things are mainly made up from compounds containing carbon, hydrogen, oxygen and nitrogen together with small amounts of other elements such as phosphorus and sulfur. The study of the chemicals of life is called biochemistry. Biochemists study proteins, carbohydrates, fats and nucleic acids.

> The word 'carbohydrate' is derived from 'carbon' and 'hydrate' (the Greek word for water).

Carbohydrates are made up of carbon, hydrogen and oxygen.

- Glucose (C$_6$H$_{12}$O$_6$) is formed during photosynthesis. Plants can convert the glucose molecules into larger molecules such as sucrose (C$_{12}$H$_{24}$O$_{12}$) or polymers such as starch and cellulose. Fig. 6.7 represents cellulose made up of glucose monomers.

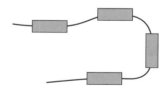

Fig. 6.7 Cellulose.

- Proteins are found everywhere in your body – your hair, skin, muscles, nails. Protein are polymers made up of monomers called amino acids. There are 20 different amino acids. Fig. 6.8 shows a diagram of a protein. Each symbol represents a different amino acid.

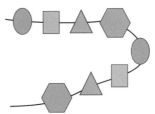

Fig. 6.8 Protein.

- Fats are solid at room temperature whereas oils are liquids. They are ester polymers made from glycerol (an alcohol) and an acid such as stearic acid. They are stored in the body and 'burn' in the body to produce energy. Fig. 6.9 represents a molecule of a fat. The brown rectangle represents glycerol and the green rectangles acids.

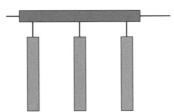

Fig. 6.9 Fats.

Your diet should contain the following percentages:

- 57% carbohydrates (sugar, sweets, bread, cakes)
- 30% fats (dairy products, oil)
- 13% protein (eggs, milk, meat, poultry, fish).

Atmosphere

Dry air consists of gases. Some of the gases are elements (for example, oxygen, nitrogen and argon) and some are compounds (for example, carbon dioxide).

Hydrosphere

The Earth's hydrosphere (oceans, rivers and lakes) consists mainly of water with some dissolved compounds. Sea water in the hydrosphere is salty because it contains dissolved salts.

How pure is our water?

OCR A   C5.1
OCR B   C4h
AQA   2.12.6
EDEXCEL 360   C3 3

> **You may live in an area where there has been a hosepipe ban.**

Water resources are limited and depend heavily upon there being sufficient rainfall.

The different types of water resources found in the United Kingdom are:
- lakes, rivers and reservoirs
- aquifers, an underground layer of rock and sand that contains water.

Water is an important resource for many important industrial chemical processes:
- a cheap raw material, e.g. for the manufacture of hydrogen
- as a coolant, e.g. in power stations to cool the towers
- as a solvent, e.g in the manufacture of soluble salts.

Water is essential to our lives so it is important to conserve water by:
- collecting rainwater in a water butt
- installing a water meter to monitor use
- not wasting water by leaving taps running, not using sprinklers. having a shower instead of a bath, placing a 'save-a-flush' or 'hippo' in the toilet cistern
- stopping leaks and dripping taps.

Some possible impurities in the domestic water supply

Some pollutants that may be found in domestic water supplies include:
- nitrate residues from the use of too much fertiliser
- pesticide residues from spraying of crops to prevent damage
- lead compounds – some parts of the country still have lead pipes. Lead is very poisonous.

> **Poison from old lead pipes is a problem in soft water areas.**

Purifying water

Water must be purified to make it fit for drinking. It could be purified by distillation, but this is a very expensive process. It is usually purified by the following processes:

1. **Filtration**. Water is filtered through sand filter beds. The layers of sand become finer towards the bottom of the beds. This process removes solid objects, however the water still contains fine particles.

2. **Sedimentation**. The fine particles are removed by adding potassium aluminium sulfate which causes the fine particles to settle.

3. **Chlorination**. The clear water from the sedimentation process contains harmful bacteria. Carefully controlled amounts of chlorine are added to kill the bacteria and other microbes.

> **Purified water is not strictly pure – it still contains many dissolved substances, and low levels of pollutants, some of which may be poisonous.**

Clean water is important for people. Millions of people in developing countries die of cholera and dysentery from drinking polluted water.

Testing for anions in water

The reactions shown in the table can be used to identify some of the anions present in water.

Anion	Test	Observation
SO_4^{2-} sulfate	Add dilute hydrochloric acid then add barium chloride solution	A white precipitate of barium sulfate is formed $Ba^{2+} + SO_4^{2-} \rightarrow BaSO_4$
Cl^- chloride	Add dilute nitric acid then silver nitrate solution	A white precipitate of silver chloride is formed $Ag^+ + Cl^- \rightarrow AgCl$
Br^- bromide	Add dilute nitric acid then silver nitrate solution	A cream precipitate of silver bromide is formed $Ag^+ + Br^- \rightarrow AgBr$
I^- iodide	Add dilute nitric acid then silver nitrate solution	A yellow precipitate of silver iodide is formed $Ag^+ + I^- \rightarrow AgI$

These reactions are examples of precipitation reactions.

Cycles in the environment

OCR A   C5.3
AQA   11.5
EDEXCEL 360   B 2 3

The following three diagrams represent the carbon cycles, the nitrogen cycle and the oxygen cycles.

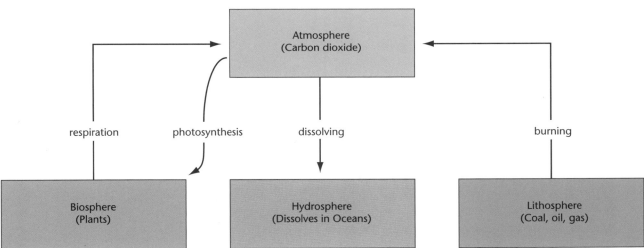

Fig. 6.11 The carbon cycle.

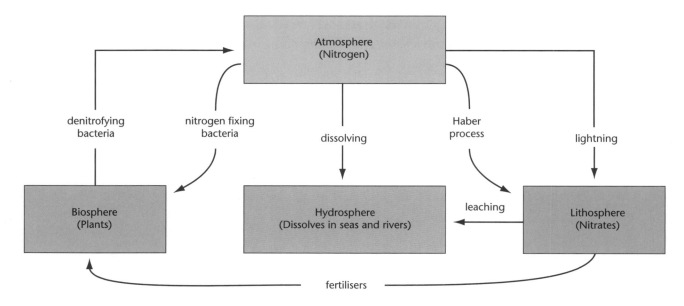

Fig. 6.12 The nitrogen cycle.

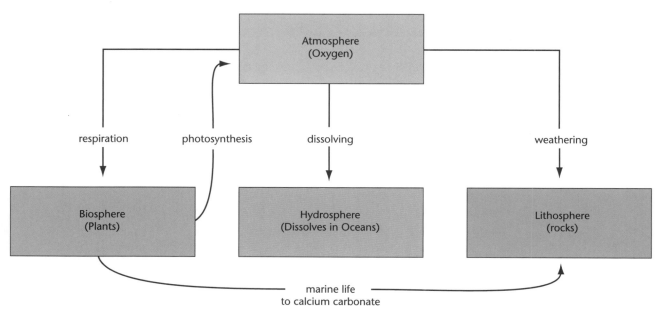

Fig. 6.13 The oxygen cycle.

HOW SCIENCE WORKS

EDEXCEL 360 C2.5

Chemistry is in fashion

It is possible to buy detergents for washing machines that are wrapped in the plastic poly(vinyl alcohol) – PVOH. The plastic is soluble in water releasing the detergent. The structure of PVOH is:

$$\left[-CH_2CH\overset{\displaystyle OH}{|} - \right]_n$$

Vinyl alcohol (hydroxyethene) is unstable; it readily changes into ethanal (CH_3CHO). Unlike most polymers, PVOH is not prepared by polymerisation of the corresponding monomer. PVOH is prepared by the hydrolysis of poly(vinyl acetate) which replaces the acetate groups (CH_3CO) with hydroxy groups (OH).

OAc OAc OAc OAc OAc OAc $\xrightarrow{\text{base}}$ OH OH OH OH OH OH

$$Ac = C\ H_3\overset{\displaystyle O}{\overset{\displaystyle \|}{C}} -$$

A leading fashion designer suggested to chemists that it should be possible to make environmentally friendly fabrics that could, after use, be changed into usable substances instead of being thrown away. Thus began the development of dissolving packaging based on polymers. When the user has finished with the packaging, it can be recycled by dissolving it in water and turning it into a form that can be recycled into a gel that can be used to germinate seeds. The same material has been used to make fabrics impregnated with coloured flowers and other shapes that slowly give off a dye as they dissolve. The shapes and dyes have different charges which makes them move as the material dissolves. These dresses could never be worn because they become sticky very quickly but they illustrate the ways in which science and art can be used to bring important issues over recyling into public debate.

The fabrics made from these plastics are often impregnated with coloured flowers and other shapes that slowly give off a dye as they dissolve. The shapes and dyes have different charges which makes them move as the material dissolves.

Supermarkets are always looking for ways to increase their profits; one of the ways of doing this is to manufacture more things that are recyclable.

Scientists working on one such project realised that plastic bottles and the synthetic materials, polyesters, were made of the same material. A simple ester is made from an acid and an alcohol.

e.g. ethanol + ethanoic acid → ethyl ethanoate + water

CH_3COOH + C_2H_5OH → $CH_3COOC_2H_5$ + H_2O

Polyesters are made from acids with two –COOH groups and alcohols with two –OH groups.

e.g. terephthalic acid + ethylene glycol → polyester + water

HOOC —⬡— COOH

benzene – 1,4 – diacarboxylic acid

HOW SCIENCE WORKS

Water is eliminated between the molecules

etcHOOC —⬡— COOH HO-CH$_2$CH$_2$-OH HOOC —⬡— COOHetc

$\downarrow$H$_2$O $\downarrow$H$_2$O $\downarrow$H$_2$O $\downarrow$H$_2$O

to form the polyester known as Terylene

etc -OC —⬡— COOHCH$_2$CH$_2$OOC —⬡— CO- etc

The name is derived from the first three letters of terephthalic and the last five letters of ethylene glycol. It is also known as polyethylene terephthalate (PET).

This is an example of **condensation polymerisation** in which small molecules such as water, ammonia and hydrogen are lost during the formation of the polymer. Polymers formed from a single monomers are called **homopolymers**, those formed from two different monomers are called copolymers.

Scientists reasoned that it should be possible to convert bottles made of polyesters into synthetic materials that could be used to make clothing. They managed to convert PET into a fabric called Greenspun©. It requires 11 two litre plastic bottles to make a fleece-type top made of Greenspun. When the top is no longer required, it can be recycled into many different things such as bowls and packaging.

It is hoped that if consumers can see that the plastics they are buying will end up as materials that can eventually be reused, they will understand the benefits of recycling.

1. Nylon has the structure:

$$\left[\begin{array}{c} \underset{\underset{H}{|}}{\overset{\overset{H}{|}}{N}}-\underset{\underset{H}{|}}{\overset{\overset{H}{|}}{C}}-\underset{\underset{H}{|}}{\overset{\overset{H}{|}}{C}}-\underset{\underset{H}{|}}{\overset{\overset{H}{|}}{C}}-\underset{\underset{H}{|}}{\overset{\overset{H}{|}}{C}}-\underset{\underset{H}{|}}{\overset{\overset{H}{|}}{C}}-\underset{\underset{H}{|}}{N}-\underset{}{\overset{\overset{O}{||}}{C}}-\underset{\underset{H}{|}}{\overset{\overset{H}{|}}{C}}-\underset{\underset{H}{|}}{\overset{\overset{H}{|}}{C}}-\underset{\underset{H}{|}}{\overset{\overset{H}{|}}{C}}-\underset{\underset{H}{|}}{\overset{\overset{H}{|}}{C}}-\overset{\overset{O}{||}}{C} \end{array} \right]_n$$

It is made by a condensation reaction between:
H$_2$NCH$_2$CH$_2$CH$_2$CH$_2$CH$_2$CH$_2$NH$_2$ and HOOCCH$_2$CH$_2$CH$_2$CH$_2$COOH.
Which simple molecule is eliminated to make nylon?

A ammonia (NH$_3$)
B carbon dioxide (CO$_2$)
C methane (CH$_4$)
D water (H$_2$O) [1]

2. **(a)** What name is given to compounds that have the same molecular formula but different structural formula?

(b) Deduce the structure of vinyl alcohol and hence suggest the structure of ethanal.

(c) Suggest why PVOH cannot be made from vinyl alcohol. [8]

3. In addition polymerisation the polymer contains the same monomer joined together many times to form a polymer. The polymer has the same empirical formula as the monomer.

(a) Write an equation to show the formation of the addition polymer poly(ethene).

(b) What is the empirical formula of PVOH? [3]

4. It has been suggested that it is more economical and environmentally friendly to buy clothes made of cotton that can be washed and reused rather than clothes made of PVOH. Give arguments for and against the use of PVOH. [5]

HOW SCIENCE WORKS Questions

Exam practice questions

1. An element has an atomic number of 5. What can be deduced from this information about its position in the periodic table?

A It is in group 3
B It is in group 5
C It is in period 3
D It is in period 5 **[1]**

2. The formula of butenedioic acid is $HOOC - CH = CH - COOH$.
Which statement is *not* true?

A It decolorises bromine water
B Its aqueous solution reacts with sodium carbonate
C Its empirical formula is the same as its molecular formula
D One mole of butenedioic acid solution will react with 2 moles of aqueous sodium hydroxide **[1]**

3. A substance **X**

(i) turned anhydrous copper(II) sulfate from white to blue
(ii) reacted with calcium to give hydrogen.
What could **X** be?

1. dilute hydrochloric acid
2. ethanol
3. water

A 1 and 2 only
B 1 and 3 only
C 2 and 3 only
D 1, 2 and 3 **[1]**

4. Choose words from the list below to fill in the gaps in the passage.

boiling	**butane**	**carbon**	**carbon dioxide**	**fuels**
general	**hydrogen**	**molecule**	**one**	**three**

The alkanes are hydrocarbons. This means they contain carbon and ____**1**____ only.
The start of each name tells us how many ____**2**____ atoms there are in one
____**3**____. Meth means ____**4**____ and _____ prop means ____**5**____.
The alkanes can be represented by the ____**6**____ formula C_nH_{2n+2}. When n = 4 the alkane is ____**7**____.
As the relative molecular mass of the alkanes increases the ____**8**____ point of the alkanes also increases.
All alkanes burn in an excess of oxygen to form ____**9**____ and water.
Alkanes are mainly used as ____**10**____. **[10]**

Exam practice questions

5. Complete the table by adding:

(i) the state of the element at room temperature and pressure (r.t.p.)
(ii) the colour of the element
(iii) the formula of the compound with sodium
(iv) the electronic configuration of the element.

Halogen	Symbol	State at r.t.p.	Formula of compound with sodium	Electronic configuration
fluorine			pale yellow	
		gas		
bromine				2 8 18 7
	I			2 8 18 18 7

[5]

6. Match each of the following ion to their test. The first one has been done for you.

Ion		Test
carbonate		Gives a white precipitate with dilute hydrochloric acid and barium chloride solution.
chloride		Gives a white precipitate with dilute nitric acid and silver nitrate solution
copper(II)		Gives a yellow colour in the flames test
iodide		Gives a yellow precipitate with dilute nitric acid and silver nitrate solution
sodium		Gives blue precipitate with sodium hydroxide solution
sulfate		Gives carbon dioxide with dilute hydrochloric acid

[6]

7. The table shows the first 5 elements of the periodic table in a spiral form.

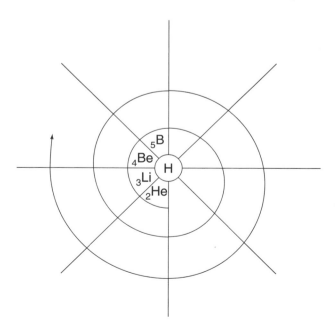

Exam practice questions

(a) Complete this table by putting in the symbols and atomic numbers for the elements up to and including element with atomic number 20. **[2]**

(b) Colour each segment as follows:
    (i) alkali metals – yellow
    (ii) halogens – green
    (iii) noble gases – blue **[3]**

(c) Expand the diagram to suggest how the transition metals could be included. **[2]**

8. The table below shows the concentration of ions in drinking water and the pH of the water from four different locations (**A**, **B**, **C** and **D**).

Location	Concentration of ions in grams per cubic metre of water				pH
	Ca^{2+}	NO_3^-	K^+	SO_4^{2-}	
A	0.35	2.3	1.6	2.2	6.7
B	4.3	0	0.2	0	8.2
C	0.25	0.15	0.5	0.5	7.0
D	2.4	0.01	0.6	0.7	7.2

(a) In which location is the water
    (i) neutral
    (i) the most alkaline?
        Suggest a reason for this value.
    (ii) most likely to be polluted by fertiliser?
        Give a reason for your answer. **[5]**

(b) Write the formulae of the two compounds that give rise to the ions found in location D.

The table below gives the pH at which certain vegetables and fruit will grow.

pH 5.25	pH 6.00	pH 6.75	pH 7.50
bilberry	broad beans	asparagus	asparagus
cranberry	gooseberry	broad beans	broccoli
gooseberry	peas	broccoli	cabbage
potato	potato	cabbage	peas
strawberries	strawberries	peas	sugar beet

[2]

(c) From the table, which fruit(s) or vegetable(s) can only be grown in a pH
    (i) less than 5.5
    (ii) greater than 7
    (iii) 5.5 to 7.5? **[4]**

Exam practice questions

9. The composition of a sample of cow's milk is:

Nutrient	Number of grams per 100 g of milk
carbohydrates	4.7 g
fats	3.4 g
minerals and vitamins	0.7 g
protein	3.2 g
water	88.0 g

(a) Describe how the presence of water can be detected in milk. You should name any reagents used and the observations made. **[2]**

(b) The main carbohydrate in milk is lactose ($C_{12}H_{22}O_{11}$). One big problem with lactose is that many people are lactose intolerant. This means that their bodies are incapable of digesting lactose. Lactose intolerant people lack the enzyme lactase which is essential for digestive hydrolysis of lactose in milk.

   (i) What is an enzyme?

   (ii) What is meant by hydrolysis?

      The hydrolysis of lactose produces glucose ($C_6H_{12}O_6$) and galactose (($C_6H_{12}O_6$))

   (iii) What name is given to substances such as glucose and galactose that have the same molecular formula but different structural formula?

   (iv) Write the equation for the hydrolysis of lactose.

      If milk is left to stand or fermented the glucose breaks down to form lactic acid.($C_3H_3O_3$)

COOH
|
C
|
CH₃

   (v) Complete the structure of lactic acid. **[8]**

(c) Most of the protein in milk is in the form of casein.

   What general name is given to the 20 monomers that make up proteins? **[1]**

(d) Milk is an emulsion containing unsaturated fats.

   (i) What is meant by an emulsion?

   (ii) Describe a test that shows that the fat in milk is unsaturated. **[4]**

(e) What element is present in milk that is essential for the growth of bones? **[1]**

Chapter 7

Calculations in Chemistry

The following topics are covered in this chapter:

- **Relative masses**
- **The mole**
- **Rates of reactions**
- **Calculations from chemical reactions**
- **Reversible reactions**
- **Fertilisers**

7.1 Relative masses

Relative atomic mass

OCR A — C6.2
OCR B — C4b
AQA — 2.12.3
EDEXCEL 360 — C2 6

Atoms are too small to be weighed individually. It is possible to compare the mass of one atom with the mass of another atom. The standard chosen is carbon-12.

> **Originally the mass of an atom was compared with the mass of a hydrogen atom which was given a unit of 1 a.m.u.. Today, carbon is used because it occurs in a vast number of compounds.**

KEY POINT
The relative atomic mass of an atom is the number of times an atom is heavier than one twelfth of a carbon-12 atom.

$$\text{Relative atomic mass} = \frac{\text{mass of one atom of the element}}{\text{mass of } \frac{1}{12} \text{ of an atom of carbon-12}}$$

Thus, magnesium has a relative atomic mass of 24 because one atom of magnesium is 24 times heavier than $\frac{1}{12}$ of an atom of carbon-12.

The relative atomic mass is a ratio and therefore has *no unit*.
The symbol for relative atomic mass is A_r.

The relative atomic masses of elements are either written as:

- A_r (Mg = 24)
- or found in the periodic table
  e.g. relative atomic mass $\longrightarrow$ $^{7}_{3}$Li (the relative atomic mass of lithium is 7)

> **You are not expected to remember the relative atomic masses of the elements.**

The relative atomic mass of an element (A_r) compares the mass of atoms of the element with the 12.00 carbon isotope. It is an average value for the isotopes of the element.

The diagram below compares the masses of different atoms relative to one another.

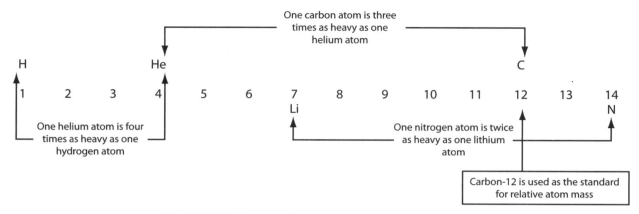

Fig. 7.1 Relative atomic masses.

Relative molecular mass

> Remember the noble gases are monatomic – one atom per molecule.

Many elements and compounds exist as molecules. Most gases are diatomic molecules (2 atoms per molecules) e.g. oxygen is O_2.

Other molecules have more than 2 atoms.

Number of atoms in molecules	Examples
3	CO_2 (carbon dioxide) H_2O (water) SO_2 (sulfur dioxide)
4	NH_3 (ammonia) SO_3 (sulfur trioxide)
5	CH_4 (methane)

Relative molecular mass is similar to relative atomic mass.

KEY POINT

Relative molecular mass M_r =

$$\frac{\text{mass of one molecule of the element or compound}}{\text{mass of } \frac{1}{12} \text{ of an atom of carbon-12}}$$

The relative molecular mass is a ratio and therefore has *no unit*.

The relative molecular mass of a molecule is calculated by adding together the relative atomic mass of each atom in its chemical formula.

> RAMs are quoted to the nearest unit, except for chlorine.

Molecule	Chemical formula	Number of atoms in one molecule	Relative molecular mass
oxygen	O_2	2 O	$2 \times 16 = \mathbf{32}$
carbon dioxide	CO_2	1 C and 2 O	$1 \times 12 + 2 \times 16 = \mathbf{44}$
water	H_2O	2 H and 1 O	$2 \times 1 + 16 = \mathbf{18}$
ammonia	NH_3	1 N and 3 H	$1 \times 14 + 3 \times 1 = \mathbf{17}$
methane	CH_4	1 C and 4 H	$1 \times 12 + 4 \times 1 = \mathbf{16}$
ethanol	C_2H_5OH	2 C, 6 H and 1 O	$2 \times 12 + 6 \times 1 + 1 \times 16 = \mathbf{46}$

Relative formula mass

 KEY POINT The relative molecular mass of ionic compounds is more accurately called relative formula mass. It has no units. It is calculated in a similar way to relative molecular mass.

Ionic compound	Chemical formula	Number of atoms in formula unit	Relative formula mass
sodium chloride	NaCl	1 Na and 1 Cl	23 + 35.5 = **58.5**
magnesium oxide	MgO	1 Mg and 1 O	$1 \times 24 + 1 \times 16 =$ **40**
calcium carbonate	CaCO$_3$	1 Ca, 1 C and 3 O	$1 \times 40 + 1 \times 12 + 3 \times 16 =$ **100**
sodium hydrogencarbonate	NaHCO$_3$	1 Na, 1 H, 1 C and 3 O	$1 \times 23 + 1 \times 1 + 1 \times 12 + 3 \times 16 =$ **84**
ammonium nitrate	NH$_4$NO$_3$	2 N, 4 H and 3 O	$2 \times 14 + 4 \times 1 + 3 \times 16 =$ **80**
copper(II) nitrate	Cu(NO$_3$)$_2$	1 Cu, 2 N and 6 O	$1 \times 64 + 2 \times 14 + 16 \times 6 =$ **188**

Percentage composition of compounds

The percentage by mass of an element in a compound can be found using the formula percentage by mass of an element in a compound =

$$\frac{\text{relative atomic mass of element (A}_r) \times \text{number of atoms in formula}}{\text{relative molecular/molecular mass (M}_r) \text{ of compound}} \times 100\%$$

e.g. What is the percentage by mass of nitrogen in (i) ammonia (NH$_3$); (ii) sodium nitrate NaNO$_3$; (iii) ammonium sulfate (NH$_4$)$_2$SO$_4$ and (iv) urea CO(NH$_2$)$_2$?

Compound	Formula	M$_r$	A$_r$ of nitrogen × number of atoms of nitrogen	% nitrogen
ammonia	NH$_3$	17	$14 \times 1 = 14$	$\frac{14}{17} \times 100 = 82.4\%$
sodium nitrate	NaNO$_3$	85	$14 \times 1 = 14$	$\frac{14}{85} \times 100 = 16.5\%$
ammonium sulfate	(NH$_4$)$_2$SO$_4$	132	$14 \times 2 = 28$	$\frac{28}{132} \times 100 = 21.2\%$
urea	CO(NH$_2$)$_2$	60	$14 \times 2 = 28$	$\frac{28}{60} \times 100 = 46.7\%$

7.2 The mole

Using moles

OCR A | C6.2
AQA | 2.12.3
EDEXCEL 360 | C2 5

Atoms are so small that they cannot be weighed. Instead we weigh a **mole** of atoms.

> **KEY POINT**
> A mole is a number and it is equal to 6×10^{23}.
> It is called Avogadro's constant or number. It is given the symbol L.

The mole is the SI unit for chemical quantity. It has the symbol **mol**.

> **KEY POINT**
> A mole of a substance contains the same number of particles as the number of atoms in 12 g of carbon-12.

To get some idea of the size of this number, if you started counting at the rate of 10 million (10 000 000) a second, it would take you 2 billion (2 000 000 000) years to count up to 6×10^{23}.

A mole of atoms of has a mass equal to the relative atomic mass of that element, but it will have the units of grams.

For example, one mole of carbon atoms has a mass of 12 g; one mole of oxygen atoms has a mass of 16 g.

The particles can be either atoms, molecules or ions.

A mole of molecules of an element or compound has a mass equal to the relative molecular mass of the element or compound.

One mole of oxygen gas (O_2) has a mass of 32 g; one mole of carbon dioxide gas has a mass of 44 g.

To calculate the number of moles in a given mass

The number of moles can be calculated using the formula:

$$\text{number of moles} = \frac{\text{mass in grams}}{\text{mass of 1 mole in grams}}$$

Empirical formula

> **KEY POINT**
> The empirical formula is the simplest formula of a compound.

The empirical formula tells you:
- the elements present in the compound
- the simplest ratio of the different types of atoms.

Formulae can be worked out using moles.

For example, 1.20 g of magnesium reacts with 0.80 g of oxygen.

	Mg	**O**
number of moles	$\frac{1.20}{24} = 0.05$	$\frac{0.80}{16} = 0.05$
molar ratio (divide by smallest)	1	1
empirical formula	**MgO**	

> The percentage of all the elements in the compound must add up to 100%.

You can use percentages of different elements to work out formulae.

	Fe	**S**	**O**
% of elements	28	24	48
number of moles	$\frac{28}{56} = 0.5$	$\frac{24}{32} = 0.75$	$\frac{48}{16} = 3$
molar ratio (divide by smallest)	1	1.5	6
make into whole numbers	2	3	12
empirical formula	$Fe_2S_3O_{12}$ or $Fe_2(SO_4)_3$		

KEY POINT The molecular formula is either the empirical formula or some multiple of it.

Substance	**Molecular formula**	**Empirical formula**
hydrogen peroxide	H_2O_2	HO
phosphorus(V) oxide	P_4O_{10}	P_2O_5
ethene	C_2H_4	CH_2

You can find the molecular formula of a compound if you know:
● the empirical formula of the substance
● the mass of 1 mole of the substance.

If the empirical formula is X_aY_b then molecular formula is $(X_aY_b)_n$, where a, b and n are whole numbers.

$$n = \frac{\text{relative molecular mass of substance}}{\text{'relative molecular mass' of empirical formula}}$$

For example, the empirical formula of a compound is CH and the mass of 1 mole is 72 g.

'relative molecular mass' of CH = 13

$n = \frac{78}{13} = 6$

Molecular formula is C_6H_6.

7.3 Calculations from chemical reactions

Using equations to calculate masses

> **KEY POINT** The relationship between the amounts in moles of reactants and products in a chemical reaction is known as the stoichiometry of the reaction.

Since matter cannot be created or destroyed, the amount of each element must be the same throughout the overall reaction, e.g. the amount of an element A on the reactant side must equal the amount of element A on the product side.

Iron reacts with sulfur to form iron(II) sulfide.

$$Fe + S \longrightarrow FeS$$

> The total mass of the reactants = the total mass of the products.

The equation tells us that:
1 mole of iron reacts with 1 mole of sulfur to form 1 mole of iron(II) sulfide
56 g of iron reacts with 32 g of sulfur to form 88 g of iron(II) sulfide.

Example 1 What mass of oxygen is given off when 2.13 g of sodium chlorate(V) is heated until no more gas is given off?

$$2NaClO_3 \longrightarrow 2NaCl + 3O_2$$

> Check 213 = 117 + 96

2 moles of sodium chlorate gives 2 moles of sodium chloride and 3 moles of oxygen
213 g of sodium chlorate(V) gives 117 g of sodium chloride and 96 g of oxygen
2.13 g of sodium chlorate gives 0.96 g of oxygen

Example 2 Calculate the percentage of water of crystallisation in magnesium sulfate crystals from the following information.

1. Mass of crucible   =   8.60 g

2. Mass of crucible + hydrated magnesium sulfate   =   12.70 g

3. Mass of crucible + anhydrous magnesium sulfate   =   10.60 g

4. Mass of water of crystallisation   =   2.10 g (2 – 3)

5. Mass of hydrated magnesium sulfate   =   4.10 g (2 – 1)

% of water of crystallisation = $\frac{2.10}{4.10} \times 100 = 51.22\%$

Limiting reactants

> **KEY POINT** The limiting reactant is the reactant that is completely used up first.

OCR B only.

Consider the reaction:

hydrogen + oxygen → water

$$2H_2 + O_2 \rightarrow 2H_2O$$

2 moles of hydrogen react with 1 mole of oxygen to form 2 moles of water. The table below shows the results of three experiments using different molar ratios of hydrogen and oxygen.

The table below shows the effects of adding too much of one of the reagents.

Experiment	Amount of reactants		Amount of products			Comment
	hydrogen	oxygen	water	unreacted hydrogen	unreacted oxygen	
1	2	1	2	0	0	All the reactants are used up
2	3	1	2	1	0	Excess hydrogen is used. Hence some is left unreacted. **Oxygen** is the limiting factor.
3	2	2	2	0	1	Excess oxygen is used. Hence some is left unreacted. **Hydrogen** is the limiting

Example

Calculate the mass of carbon dioxide formed when 0.1 moles of calcium carbonate reacts with 0.15 moles of hydrochloric acid.

calcium carbonate + hydrochloric acid → calcium chloride + water + carbon dioxide

$$CaCO_3 \quad + \quad 2HCl \quad \rightarrow \quad CaCl_2 \quad + H_2O + \quad CO_2$$

From the equation, 1 mole of calcium carbonate reacts with 2 moles of hydrochloric acid, therefore 0.1 mole of calcium carbonate reacts with 0.2 moles of hydrochloric acid.

There are only 0.15 moles of hydrochloric acid, so this is the limiting reactant.

From the equation, 2 moles of hydrochloric acid gives 1 mole of carbon dioxide, therefore 0.15 moles will give 0.075 moles of carbon dioxide.

mass of carbon dioxide formed = $0.075 \times 44 = 3.30$ g.

7 Calculations in Chemistry

Volume changes in chemical reactions

AQA   2.12.3

It is easier to measure the volume of a gas than the mass of gas.

> **KEY POINT**
>
> 1 mole of molecules of any gas occupies 24 000 cm³ (24 dm³) at room temperature and pressure. This can be restated as 'equal volumes of gases at the same temperature and pressure contain the same number of molecules.'

Room temperature and pressure are 25°C and 1 atmosphere.

The equation $C + O_2 \rightarrow CO_2$ tells us that:

1 mole of carbon (12 g) reacts with 1 mole of oxygen (24 dm³) to form 1 mole of carbon dioxide (24 dm³)

The volume of a gas can be calculated from its mass.

Example 1 What is the volume of 11.0 g of carbon dioxide?

Firstly, work out the relative molecular mass of carbon dioxide = $12 + 2 \times 16 = 44$

Work out the number of moles of carbon dioxide $\frac{11}{44} = 0.25$ moles

Multiply the answer by 24 dm³ = $0.25 \times 24 =$ **6 dm³**

Similarly the mass of a gas can be worked out from its volume.

Example 2 What is the mass of 12.0 dm³ of chlorine (Cl_2)?

Work out the number of moles of chlorine by dividing the volume (in dm³) by 24

$= \frac{12}{24} = 0.5$

Multiply the number of moles by the relative molecular mass of chlorine ($2 \times 35.5 = 71$)
Mass = $0.5 \times 71 =$ **35.5 g**

Atom economy (or efficiency)

AQA   2.12.3
EDEXCEL 360 C2 5

In 1998, Barry Trost was awarded the 'Presidential Green Chemistry Challenge Award' for his concept of atom economy.

The aim of green chemistry is to reduce the amount of waste caused in industrial processes. Reactions in which a large proportion of the reactant atoms end up in waste products:
- contribute to pollution
- make ineffective use of resources
- raise the costs of production
- have to be disposed of.

The atom economy (atom utilisation) is a measure of the amount of starting materials that end up as useful products.

$$\text{atom economy} = \frac{\text{total relative molecular masses of useful products}}{\text{total relative molecular mass of reactants}} \times 100\%$$

Consider the manufacture of calcium oxide (quicklime) from limestone:

$$CaCO_3 \longrightarrow CaO + CO_2$$

relative molecular masses   100   56   44

In this process, the carbon dioxide is allowed to escape into the atmosphere.

$$\text{atom economy} = \frac{56}{100} \times 100 = 56\%$$

In this reaction, 44% of the reactants are wasted.

To increase atom efficiency, chemists try to make use of the other products of the reaction and find an alternative way of making the required product.

Ethanol can be made from either sugar ($C_6H_{12}O_6$) or by reacting ethene with water.

(i) From sugar:

$$C_6H_{12}O_6 \longrightarrow 2C_2H_5OH + 2CO_2$$

M_r 180   92   88

$$\text{atom economy} = \frac{92}{180} \times 100 = 51.1\%$$

In this reaction, 48.9% of the reactants are wasted.

(ii) From ethene:

$$C_2H_4 + H_2O \longrightarrow C_2H_5OH$$

M_r 28   18   46

$$\text{atom economy} = \frac{46}{46} \times 100 = 100\%$$

KEY POINT   **Reactions in which there is only one product are 100% efficient.**

There are, however, other points to consider such as:
- cost of products
- cost of running the process
- yield
- are reactants renewable?

Note: if the 'other' products can be used to make useful products, they are known as **by-products**. If, on the other hand, they have to be disposed of, they are **waste products**.

Percentage yield

Most reactions do not go to completion. The actual yield of a reaction is almost always less than the theoretical yield.

$$\text{Percentage yield} = \frac{\text{actual yield}}{\text{predicted yield}} \times 100$$

Example 1 What is the percentage yield if 3.0 grams of hydrogen reacts with nitrogen to form 10.2 grams of ammonia?

$$N_2 + 3H_2 \rightarrow 2NH_3$$

From the equation, 3 moles of hydrogen produces 2 moles of ammonia, therefore 6 g (3 × 2) of hydrogen should produce 34 grams (2 × 17) of ammonia.

3.0 grams of hydrogen should produce $\dfrac{34 \times 3.0}{6} = 17.0\,\text{g}$ (predicted yield)

$$\text{percentage yield} = \frac{10.2}{17} \times 100 = 60.0\%$$

Example 2 What is the percentage yield if 9.0 grams of hydrogen reacted with nitrogen to form 30.6 grams of ammonia under the same conditions as in example 1?

$$\text{predicted yield} = \frac{34 \times 9}{6} = 51.0\,\text{g}$$

$$\text{percentage yield} = \frac{30.6}{51.0} \times 100 = 60.0\%$$

 KEY POINT Increasing the amount of reactants increases the amount of product but the percentage yield remains the same under the same conditions.

 KEY POINT The percentage yield is always between 0% and 100%. 100% yield means that no product has been lost and 0% yield means that no product has been made.

Because atoms cannot be created or destroyed, no atoms are gained or lost in a chemical reaction. However, it is not always possible to obtain the calculated amount of a product because:

- the reaction may not go to completion because it is reversible
- some of the product may be lost when it is prepared and separated from the reaction mixture, e.g. loss in separation, loss in evaporation, loss in transferring liquids and loss in heating
- some of the reactants may react in ways different to the expected reaction, e.g. reacting ethanol with concentrated sulfuric acid under different conditions can produce:

  – ethene

  – diethyl ether

  – ethyl hydrogensulfate.

Concentration of solutions

OCR A   C6.2

The concentration of a solution can be measured in either g/dm^3 or mol/dm^3. Chemists prefer to use mol/dm^3 because it gives an idea of the number of particles in solution.

> **KEY POINT** When 1 mole of solute is dissolved in water and the solution made up to a volume of $1.0\ dm^3$ the solution has a concentration of 1 mole per dm^3. This is written as $1.0\ mol/dm^3$ or 1.0 m. It is called a molar solution.

$1000\ cm^3 = 1\ dm^3$

Equal volumes of solutions of the same molar concentration contain the same number of moles of solute.

To convert g/dm^3 concentrations to mol/dm^3 concentration, the mass is divided by the relative molecular mass of the solute.

Example 1 A solution contains $73.0\ g$ of hydrochloric acid (HCl) in $1\,dm^3$ of solution. What is the concentration of this solution in mol/dm^3?

M_r of HCl = 1 + 35.5 = 36.5

Concentration $= \dfrac{73.0}{36.5} = \mathbf{2.0\ mol/dm^3}$

Example 2 A solution contains $4.0\ g$ of sodium hydroxide (NaOH) dissolved in $250\ cm^3$ of solution. What is the concentration of this solution in mol/dm^3?

If $4.0\ g$ of sodium hydroxide is dissolved in $250\ cm^3$ of solution then $16.0\ g$ of sodium hydroxide will dissolve in $1000\ cm^3$ ($1.0\ dm^3$) solution:

M_r of NaOH = 23 + 16 + 1 = 40

Concentration in $= \dfrac{16.0}{40} = \mathbf{0.4\ mol/dm^3}$

To convert mol/dm^3 concentrations to g/dm^3 concentration, the number of moles in solution is multiplied by the relative molecular mass of the solute.

Example 3 What is the concentration in g/dm^3 of sulfuric acid in $0.1\ mol/dm^3$ sulfuric acid (H_2SO_4)?

M_r of H_2SO_4 = 2 × 1 + 32 + 4 × 16 = 98

Concentration in g/dm^3 = 0.1 × 98 = **9.8 g/dm³**

Example 4 What is the concentration in g/dm^3 of potassium hydroxide (KOH) if $250\ cm^3$ of solution contained 0.1 moles of potassium hydroxide?

Number of moles of KOH in $250\ cm^3$ = 0.1 mole

Number of moles of KOH in $1000\ cm^3$ ($1\ dm^3$) = 0.1 × 4 = 0.4 moles

M_r of KOH = 39 + 16 + 1 = 56

Concentration in g/dm^3 = 0.4 x 56 = **22.4 g**

Diluting solutions

> **KEY POINT** When diluting solutions, always add the more concentrated solution to the solvent (usually water).

> **OCR B only**

Example 1 How would you convert $1.0 \, mol/dm^3$ hydrochloric acid to $0.5 \, mol/dm^3$ hydrochloric acid?

The dilution factor is: $\dfrac{1.0}{0.5} = 2$

So take 1 part of water (e.g. $10 \, cm^3$) and add 1 part of $1.0 \, mol/dm^3$ hydrochloric acid ($10 \, cm^3$) to give $0.5 \, mol/dm^3$ hydrochloric acid.

Example 2 How would you convert $1.0 \, mol/dm^3$ hydrochloric acid to $0.1 \, mol/dm^3$ hydrochloric acid?

The dilution factor is: $\dfrac{1.0}{0.1} = 10$

So take 9 parts of water (e.g. $90 \, cm^3$) and add 1 part of $1.0 \, mol/dm^3$ hydrochloric acid ($10 \, cm^3$) to give $0.1 \, mol/dm^3$ hydrochloric acid.

We use dilution in everyday living:
- diluting concentrated orange juice
- diluting liquid medicines
- diluting windscreen washing liquid for different temperatures.

Dilution is particularly important in medication. If the wrong dose is given, it can cause complicated side effects – in some cases it can be fatal.

Recommended daily allowance

Food packaging contains information about the recommended daily allowance of substances in the food.

> **Recommended daily allowance is abbreviated to RDA.**

You may have seen labels on foods similar to the one in the diagram. The label will also give the RDA for each of the ingredients. The RDA for sodium is 2400 mg. This food contains 470 mg sodium, which is about 20% of the RDA.

Total Fat 12 g	18%
Saturated Fat 3 g	15%
Cholesterol 30 mg	10%
Sodium 470 mg	20%

The amount of salt (sodium chloride) required to produce 470 mg is calculated as follows:

$$Na^+ + Cl^- \longrightarrow NaCl$$

1 mole of sodium (ions) is obtained from 1 mole of sodium chloride
i.e. 23 g of sodium (ions) is obtained from 58.5 g of sodium chloride

470 mg of sodium (ions) is obtained from $\dfrac{58.5 \times 1000}{23 \times 1000} \times 470 = 1194.4 \, mg$
i.e. about 1.2 g

Note that the sodium (ions) may come from different sources.

Titrations

KEY POINT In titration experiments, the volume of solution required to completely react with a known volume of another solution is determined.

Titrations involving an acid and an alkali (soluble base) are called acid base titrations.

1 A known amount of alkali (usually 25.0 cm³) is placed in a conical flask using a pipette.

2 Two drops of an indicator (phenolphthalein or methyl orange) are added to this solution.

3 An acid of known concentration is put in a burette.

4 The acid is added until the indicator just changes colour.

5 The volumes of acid used is read and recorded.

6 The experiment is repeated until at least two readings are the same or within 0.05 cm³ of one another.

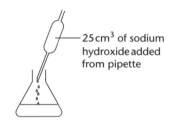
25 cm³ of sodium hydroxide added from pipette

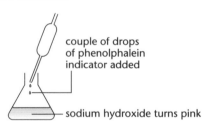
couple of drops of phenolphalein indicator added

sodium hydroxide turns pink

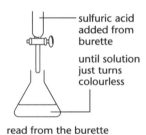
sulfuric acid added from burette

until solution just turns colourless

read from the burette the volume of acid added

Sample results:

Volume before in cm³	0.00	0.20	0.00	
Volume after in cm³	25.40	25.50	25.35	Average
Volume added in cm³	25.40	25.30	25.35	25.35

Fig. 7.2 Performing a titration.

The equation for the reaction is
$$2NaOH + H_2SO_4 \rightarrow Na_2SO_4 + 2H_2O$$

From the results we can see that:

25.35 cm³ of 0.05 mol/dm³ of sulfuric acid reacted with 25.0 cm³ of sodium hydroxide solution.

> This is a neutralisation reaction. The ionic equation is
> $H^+ + OH^- \rightarrow H_2O$

Moles of sulfuric acid used $= \dfrac{25.35 \times 0.5}{1000} = 0.0127$

Since 1 mole of sulfuric acid reacts with 2 moles of sodium hydroxide, the number of moles of sodium hydroxide in 25.0 cm³ = 2 x 0.0127 = 0.0254 moles

number of moles in 1000 cm³ of solution $= \dfrac{0.0254 \times 1000}{25} = \textbf{0.01 mol/dm}^3$

7.4 Rates of reactions

Reactions at different rates

OCR A | C6.2
AQA | 12.5
EDEXCEL 360 | C2 8

KEY POINT The rate of a reaction measures the rate of disappearance of the reactant or the rate of appearance of a product.

$$\text{Rate of reaction} = \frac{\text{amount of reactant used up or amount of product formed}}{\text{time}}$$

Some reactions are very slow and other reactions are very fast:

Some textbooks refer to 'rate of reaction' as 'speed of reaction'.

- rusting is a slow reaction
- burning and explosions are very fast reactions.

Measuring rate of reaction

	Reaction in which amount of reactant is used up	Reaction in which amount of product is formed
Reaction studied	Marble chips and hydrochloric acid	Reaction in which amount of product is formed
Equation and what is measured	$CaCO_3 + 2HCl \rightarrow CaCl_2 + H_2O + CO_2$ Total loss in mass of calcium carbonate and HCl	Magnesium and hydrochloric acid $Mg + 2HCl \rightarrow MgCl_2 + H_2$ Total volume of hydrogen given off
Apparatus	 dilute hydrochloric acid, cotton wool, conical flask, marble chips, stopwatch, electronic balance	gas syringe, conical flask, small test tube containing magnesium ribbon, dilute hydrochloric acid
Method	1 Set up apparatus as shown (the cotton wool is to stop any acid splashing out). 2 Record the mass of the whole system. 3 Add the marble chips. 4 Immediately start stopwatch. 5 Record the mass of the system at half minute intervals.	1 Clean a piece of magnesium ribbon. 2 Place in small test tube. 3 Set up apparatus as shown. 4 Shake flask to mix magnesium and acid. 5 Immediately start stopwatch. 6 Record the volume of hydrogen given off every half minute.
Graphs from the results	(graph: total mass of system/g vs time/min; curve decreasing from 60 to below 58; reaction stops)	(graph: total volume of hydrogen/cm³ vs time/min; curve increasing to 35; reaction stops)
Explanation and rate	The system loses mass because carbon dioxide is given off. The rate can be found by drawing tangents at various points. $\text{Rate} = \dfrac{\text{loss of mass in system}}{\text{time}}$	The total volume of hydrogen given off increases with time. The rate can be found by drawing tangents at various points. $\text{Rate} = \dfrac{\text{volume of hydrogen given off}}{\text{time}}$

> **A reaction stops when one of the reactants is used up.**

For practical reasons, reactions used in the laboratory for studying rate of reaction must not be too fast or too slow.

Other methods of measuring rate of reaction include:
- colour changes
- formation of a precipitate
- pH changes
- temperature changes
- time taken for a given mass of solid to react.

Factors affecting rate of reaction

The table below compares some of the factors that affect the rate of a chemical reaction.

Factor	Reactions affected	Change made in the condition	Effect on rate of reaction
catalyst	slow reactions that can be speeded up by adding a suitable catalyst	reduces the amount of energy required for the reaction to take place	increases rate of reaction
concentration	all reactions	increase in concentration of one of the reactants	increases the rate of the reaction
light	wide variety of reactions including reactions with mixtures of gases including chlorine and bromine	reaction in sunlight or UV light	greatly increases rate of reaction
particle size	reactions involving solids and liquids; solids and gases or mixtures of solids	make solid particles smaller, e.g. use powdered form of solid	greatly increases the rate of reaction
pressure	reactions involving gases	increase the pressure	greatly increases the rate of reaction
temperature	all reactions	increase by 10°C decrease by 10°C	approximately doubles rate approximately halves rate

Explaining different rates using particle model

The collision theory states that:
- chemical reactions can only occur when reacting particles collide with each other
- have a certain sufficient minimum energy called the activation energy.

Change	Before	After
increase surface area • more collisions • reaction faster		
increase concentration • more collisions between particles • more collisions leading to reactions • reaction faster		
increase temperature • particles move faster • more collisions and more energetic • reaction faster		

Increasing pressure has the same effect.

Sunlight and UV light have the same effect.

The table shows how changing surface area, concentration and temperature affects the reaction rates.

Catalyst

 KEY POINT

A catalyst is a substance that changes the rate of a chemical reaction but it is not used up during the reaction:

• different reactions need different catalysts

• catalysts are important in increasing the rates of chemical reactions used in industrial processes to reduce costs.

Rates of reaction in everyday life

Enzymes work best at 37°C (body temperature). At high temperatures enzymes are destroyed (denatured).

We use rate of reaction in everyday life:

● the speed of cooking is increased by using a pressure cooker

● rusting is slowed down by covering iron objects with paint and oil

● tablets dissolve more quickly if they are powdered.

● enzymes are biological catalysts, and they are important in speeding up chemical reactions to the maintenance of life.

Enzymes are also used:

● in the manufacture of alcohol from sugar

● making cheese and yoghurt

● in washing powders to break down protein stains such as blood.

7.5 Reversible reactions

Equilibrium

OCR B   C4d
AQA   2.12.3
EDEXCEL 360   C2 8

Many chemical reactions only go in one direction. The reaction cannot be reversed to obtain the original reactants, e.g. copper(II) sulfate reacts with sodium hydroxide to form copper(II) hydroxide and sodium sulfate.

$$CuSO_4 + 2NaOH \rightarrow Cu(OH)_2 + Na_2SO_4$$

Some chemical reactions can be reversed. The products of the reaction can react to produce the original reactants. Such reactions are called reversible reactions and can be represented as:

$$A + B \rightleftharpoons C + D$$

The sign $\rightleftharpoons$ means the reaction is reversible.

For example, ammonia gas reacts with hydrogen chloride gas to form ammonium chloride solid.

$$NH_3 + HCl \rightarrow NH_4Cl$$

When ammonium chloride is gently heated, it decomposes into ammonia and hydrogen chloride.

$$NH_4Cl \rightarrow NH_3 + HCl$$

Thus we can write the reversible reaction:

$$NH_3 + HCl \rightleftharpoons NH_4Cl$$

Chemists call the reaction from:
● left to right the **forward reaction**
● right to left the **reverse reaction**.

Dynamic equilibrium

If a reversible reaction takes place in a closed system, a state of balance or equilibrium is reached.

A closed system is a system where the reactants and the products cannot escape.

When the system reaches dynamic equilibrium:
● the rate of the forward reaction = rate of the reverse reaction
● the percentages of the reactants and products remains constant.

If the conditions, such as temperature or pressure, are altered, then the amounts of the reactants and products will change. A reversible reaction does not go to completion but the conditions can be selected so that the reaction can still be used efficiently.

Haber process for making ammonia

OCR B   C4d
AQA   C12.5
EDEXCEL 360   C2 8

KEY POINT Ammonia NH$_3$ is a compound of nitrogen and hydrogen. It is produced in large quantities by the Haber process. Ammonia is manufactured from nitrogen and hydrogen in a process known as the Haber process. Nitrogen is obtained from air and hydrogen from methane.

This diagram summarises the process.

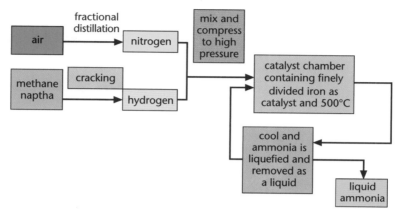

The equation for the reaction is:

$$N_2 + 3H_2 \rightarrow 2NH_3 \quad \text{exothermic}$$

By choosing the best conditions, chemists can produce the highest **yield** of ammonia in a reasonable length of time.

The conditions for the Haber process are:
- excess nitrogen (the equilibrium will shift to the right to remove the nitrogen)
- high pressure (there are 4 molecules of gas on the left-hand side and 2 molecules of gas on the right-hand side). The equilibrium will shift to the right to reduce the pressure
- low temperature (since the forward reaction is exothermic, the equilibrium will shift in the exothermic direction)
- iron catalyst (a low temperature slows down the reaction, using a catalyst speeds up the reaction).

KEY POINT In practice, the Haber process operates at 200 atmosphere pressure, a temperature of about 450°C, and uses an iron catalyst.

Uses of ammonia

Ammonia is used for:
- the manufacture of fertilisers
- the manufacture of nitric acid
- cleaning fluids.

The continued growth in the world's population is putting a strain on available food resources. Fertilisers, made from ammonia, are one class of chemicals that are widely used to improve the yield of crops from a given area of land.

Continuous and batch processes

There are two main types of chemical processes – continuous and batch.

Ammonia and ethanol (from ethene) are made using a continuous process. Special chemicals such as certain medicines, pharmaceutical drugs and ethanol (from sugar) are made by a batch process.

	Continuous process	Batch process
automation	tend to be automatic	tends to be labour intensive
quality of product	pure and consistent	can vary
start-up costs	very high	low
time	never stops	time lapse between making each batch
type of product	only one product	can be a variety of products

The cost of making and developing a medicine or pharmaceutical drug include:
- research and testing
- labour costs
- energy costs
- raw materials
- time taken for development
- marketing.

Many useful drugs have been found in plants.

> **Foxgloves are grown commercially for the pharmaceutical industry.**

Plant	Use	Active ingredient
bark of white willow	cures headaches	salicylic acid (similar to aspirin)
foxglove	heart disease	digoxin
Madagascar periwinkle	myela (cancer)	vinblastine
aloe	burns	aloectin B
Chinese wormwood	treatment of malaria	artemisinin

Raw materials for speciality chemicals, such as pharmaceuticals, can be either made synthetically or extracted from plants. Chinese wormwood takes 18 months to grow and large harvests are required to help solve the problem of malaria. This is a costly and labour intensive process.

Drugs are extracted from plants by:
- first crushing the plant to a pulp
- dissolving the drug in a suitable solvent – usually an organic solvent
- extracting the drug using chromatography.

> **The Chinese discovered the use of Chinese wormwood over 2000 years ago.**

The drug, artemether, a derivative of artemisinin, has been synthesised and is used to treat malaria. Making a successful new drug can be very lucrative, but the costs of development are high.

The costs involve:
- payment to the developers
- less automation until full scale manufacture
- the research and testing which may take many years
- the raw materials are likely to be rare and/or involve expensive extraction from plants
- legislative demands. (Some drugs have unexpected side effects, e.g. the anti-depressant drug Prozac, can trigger suicidal thoughts.)

The following factors determine the development of new drugs:
- research and development time and associated labour costs
- time required to meet legal requirements including timescale for testing and human trials
- anticipated demand for new product
- length of pay back time for initial investment.

A drug patent lasts for only 20 years. A drug company has to recover its costs in that time and make a profit for further research.

The cost of failure can be very high. The development of torcetrapid, a heart disease drug, was withdrawn after it was found to increase the number of deaths from heart disease. The company had spent about £500 million on the project.

Chemical synthesis

OCR A   **C6.2**
EDEXCEL 360 **C2 5**

All the products we use, such as food additives, fertilisers, dyestuffs, paints, pigments and pharmaceuticals are obtained from the air, crude oil, minerals and water.

Before an inorganic substance can be made, it has to go through the following processes:
- choosing the reaction or series of reactions to make the required product. Obviously it is better if the product can be made in one stage with little or no waste products
- carrying out a risk assessment. This means:
  - identifying the hazards
  - deciding who might be harmed and how
  - evaluating the risks and decide on precautions
  - recording the findings and implementing them
  - reviewing the assessment and updating if necessary
- working out the quantities of reactants to use, see 7.3.
- carrying out the reaction in suitable apparatus in the right conditions (such as temperature, concentration or the presence of a catalyst). This is particularly true for reversible reactions (see page 119)
- separating the product from the reaction mixture
- purifying the product
- measuring the yield and checking the purity of the product.

7.6 *Fertilisers*

Composition of fertilisers

OCR A — C6.1
OCR B — C4c
AQA — 2.12.6
EDEXCEL 360 — C2 8

KEY POINT Fertilisers are chemicals that provide plants with essential chemical elements.

The essential elements for a plant to grow are nitrogen, phosphorus and potassium. These essential elements can be obtained from either natural sources or artificial sources.

The table below summarises the importance of these elements.

Element	Importance to growing plant	Natural sources	Artificial source
nitrogen	for growth of stems and leaves	manure, bird droppings, dried blood	ammonium nitrate, ammonium sulfate, urea
phosphorus	for root growth	bone meal	ammonium phosphate
potassium	for flowers and fruit	wood ash	potassium sulfate

Fertilisers must be soluble in water. They are used:
● to replace elements used up by previous crops
● to add more nitrogen so plants increase in growth.

The equations refer to the numbered steps in the flow diagram.

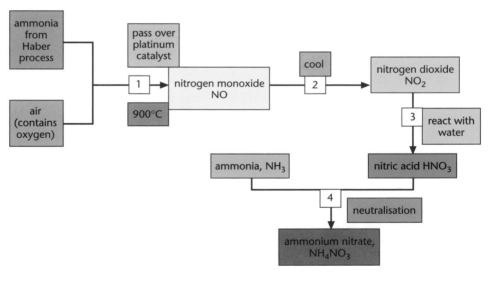

The figure above summarises how the fertiliser ammonium nitrate is made.

The equations for the reactions are:

1. ammonia + oxygen → nitrogen monoxide + water
$$4NH_3 + 5O_2 \rightarrow 4NO + 6H_2O$$

2. nitrogen monoxide + oxygen → nitrogen dioxide
$$2NO \quad + \quad O_2 \quad \rightarrow \quad 2NO_2$$

3. nitrogen dioxide + water + oxygen $\longrightarrow$ nitric acid

$$4NO_2 \quad + \quad 2H_2O \ + \ O_2 \ \longrightarrow \quad 4HNO_3$$

4. nitric acid + ammonia $\longrightarrow$ ammonium nitrate

$$HNO_3 \quad + \quad NH_3 \quad \longrightarrow \qquad NH_4NO_3$$

Choosing the materials Ammonium nitrate is made from concentrated nitric acid and dry ammonia.

$$HNO_3 + NH_3 \longrightarrow NH_4NO_3$$

Identifying the hazards Nitric acid is harmful, corrosive and an oxidising agent. Ammonia is toxic and corrosive. The product, ammonium nitrate is an oxidising agent and harmful. In certain conditions it explodes. Ammonium nitrate is covered with a conditioning agent to improve its safe handling and storage and to reduce the possibility of explosions.

Quantities of reactants to use From the equation, 63 g of nitric acid reacts with 24 dm^3 of ammonia to produce 80 g of ammonium nitrate.

Reaction apparatus and conditions The building must be made of materials that do not burn. The working area must be kept clear of all combustible materials. The ammonium nitrate must not be allowed to escape from the process. The factory must have a non-smoking policy.

Separating the product from the reaction mixture The ammonium nitrate solution formed is carefully evaporated to dryness.

Purifying ammonium nitrate Not required, the ammonium nitrate is about 99% pure.

The yield and purity of ammonium nitrate The ammonium nitrate is almost 100% pure and the yield very close to 100%.

Other fertilisers that can be made from ammonia are ammonium sulfate, ammonium phosphate and urea.

The table below shows the percentages by mass of nitrogen, phosphorus and potassium in various fertilisers.

Compound	Formula	M_r	% nitrogen	% phosphorus	% potassium
ammonia	NH_3	17	$\frac{14}{17} \times 100 = 82.4\%$	0	0
ammonium phosphate	$(NH_4)_3PO_4$	149	$\frac{42}{149} \times 100 = 28.2\%$	$\frac{31}{149} \times 100 = 20.8\%$	0
ammonium sulfate	$(NH_4)_2SO_4$	132	$\frac{28}{132} \times 100 = 21.2\%$	0	0
potassium nitrate	KNO_3	101	$\frac{14}{101} \times 100 = 13.9\%$	0	$\frac{39}{101} \times 100 = 38.6\%$
urea	$CO(NH_2)_2$	60	$\frac{28}{60} \times 100 = 46.7\%$	0	0

Overuse of fertilisers

Too much fertiliser can be harmful. When it rains, fertilisers can be washed out of the soil and end up in ponds, lakes and rivers. This leads to eutrophication. Eutrophication describes the following process:

- fertilisers cause water plants and algae to grow rapidly
- they cover the surface of the water
- which stops photosynthesis
- and reduces dissolved oxygen in the water
- plant material dies and decomposes
- aerobic bacteria use up oxygen
- causing fish and other river life to die.

Sewage escaping into ponds, lakes and rivers causes a similar problem.

Yields of crops are reduced by pests and disease. Intensive farmers use pesticides such as insecticides (which kill insect pests, e.g. mosquitoes), rodenticides (for killing rodents such as rats and mice) and herbicides (for killing unwanted plants and weeds) to improve the quantity of their crops. Organic farmers have to use different methods such as:

- rotation of crops
- growing resistant crop varieties.
- ensuring that plants are strong and healthy
- using physical means such as grease bands on trees trunks and copper bands around the stems of plants
- using biological pest controls such as nematodes
- using sprays made from chemicals found in plants such as rotenone (obtained from tropical plants) and pyrethrum (obtained from foxgloves).

Farmers have to follow the UK national standards if they want to claim that their products are organic.

AQA   2.12.6
EDEXCEL 360   C2 8

HOW SCIENCE WORKS

Hydrogen as a fuel of the future

It has been suggested that using hydrogen can reduce:
- our dependence on petroleum for fuel
- pollution
- greenhouse gas emissions.

Some of the uses of hydrogen are:
- to produce fertilisers
- to hydrogenate fats and oils
- as a rocket fuel
- the manufacture of hydrochloric acid.

Hydrogen is mainly manufactured by the steam reforming of natural gas. In this process, under the conditions of high temperatures (700–1100°C) and in the presence of a metal catalyst, steam reacts with methane to produce carbon monoxide and hydrogen.

New sources of hydrogen will be needed in the future. The answer could be to use hydrogen produced from water, using nuclear energy to produce either electrical energy or thermochemical energy.

Electrical energy

Nuclear energy is used to produce electrical energy which, in turn, separates water into hydrogen and oxygen by electrolysis. This process is about 25% efficient.

Thermochemical energy

Thermochemical water-splitting is the conversion of water into hydrogen and oxygen by a series of chemical reactions. In one such series:

Iodine and sulfur dioxide are added to water, forming hydrogen iodide and sulfuric acid in an exothermic reaction. Under suitable conditions, these compounds are immiscible and can be separated.

Reaction 1 $I_2 + SO_2 + 2H_2O \rightarrow 2HI + H_2SO_4$ *Exothermic*

The sulfuric acid is decomposed at about 830°C releasing oxygen and recycling sulfur dioxide

Reaction 2 $2H_2SO_4 \rightarrow 2SO_2 + 2H_2O + O_2$ *Endothermic*

Hydrogen iodide is decomposed at about 350°C, releasing the hydrogen and recycling the iodine

Reaction 3 $2HI \rightarrow I_2 + H_2$ *Endothermic*

The overall reaction is the decomposition of water into hydrogen and oxygen

$$2H_2O \rightarrow 2H_2 + O_2$$

Nuclear energy is used to produce heat energy which is used for the decomposition reactions 2 and 3.

HOW SCIENCE WORKS

The process is shown in the following cycle diagram. The conditions above the arrows show that energy is required; the conditions below the arrow show the energy that is given out.

The process takes in water at a high temperature heat and releases hydrogen and oxygen at a low temperature heat. All the reagents are recycled and there are no effluents.

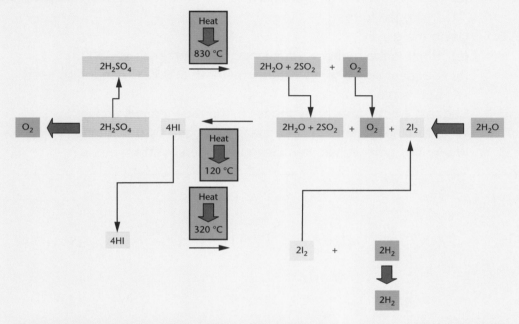

The decomposition of sulfuric acid and hydrogen iodide need a high temperature.

The graph below plots the temperature produced by the nuclear energy plant against the percentage yield of hydrogen.

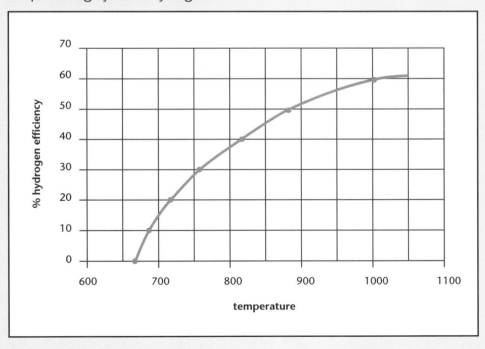

7 Calculations in Chemistry

1. **(a)** What is natural gas?
    (b) Write an equation for the production of hydrogen from natural gas
    by the steam reforming process. **[2]**

2. What is the reaction involving hydrogen gas in the manufacture of
    fertilisers? **[1]**

3. Why is the manufacturing plant made of stainless steel and not an
    unreactive thermoplastic? **[2]**

4. State, with a reason:
    (a) whether the iodine in reaction 1 has been oxidised or reduced
    (b) if, in reaction 3, an increase in pressure would increase the amount of
    hydrogen formed. **[3]**

5. Using the graph:
    (a) What is the hydrogen efficiency of the process at 830°C?
    (b) Suggest why a temperature greater than 900°C cannot be used
    in this process. **[3]**

6. Suggest what is meant by the term 'thermochemical energy'. **[1]**

7. What are the advantages of making hydrogen by this method? **[3]**

8. What risks are involved in making hydrogen by this method? **[2]**

Exam practice questions

1. The formula of aluminium silicate (china clay) was written as $Al_2O_3.2SiO_2.2H_2O$. Its modern formula is $Al_2(OH)_xSi_2O_y$. What are the values of x and y?

	x	y
A	3	3
B	3	5
C	4	3
D	4	5

   [1]

2. Dilute sulfuric acid reacts with copper(II) oxide according to the equation:

   $$CuO + H_2SO_4 \rightarrow CuSO_4 + H_2O$$

   What does not alter the rate of this reaction?
   A   concentration of sulfuric acid
   B   pressure
   C   size of copper(II) oxide particles
   D   temperature

   [1]

3. The four equations show the overall equations for four possible ways of making fertilisers. The relative formula mass of each fertiliser is:

   $NH_4NO_3 = 80$; $(NH_4)_2SO_4 = 132$; $(NH_4)_3PO_4 = 149$; $Ca(H_2PO_4)_2 = 234$

   Which reaction will produce the greatest mass of fertiliser from the same mass of sulfuric acid?
   A $H_2SO_4 + 2NH_3 \rightarrow (NH_4)_2SO_4$
   B $H_2SO_4 + 2NH_3 + 2NaNO_3 \rightarrow 2NH_4NO_3 + Na_2SO_4$
   C $2H_2SO_4 + Ca_3(PO_4)_2 \rightarrow Ca(H_2PO_4)_2 + 2CaCO_4$
   D $3H_2SO_4 + Ca_3(PO_4)_2 + 6NH_3 \rightarrow 2(NH_4)_3PO_4 + 3CaSO_4$ [1]

4. Choose words from the list below to fill in the gaps in the passage.

   > activation   catalyst   collide   concentrated   energy
   > increases   size   surface   temperature   unchanged

   For particles to react they must ____1____ with each other. Only particles with a certain amount of energy called the ____2____ energy react.
   If the ____3____ of the reacting particles is decreased, there is more ____4____ area available for reacting and the speed of the reaction____5____.
   When a solution becomes more ____6____ the number of particles present increases.
   Increasing the ____7____ increases the rate of the reaction.
   One of the ways a ____8____ is thought to work is by lowering the ____9____ required before the reaction takes place. It speeds up the reaction but is ____10____ at the end of the reaction.

   [10]

Exam practice questions

5. Match each of the following with their definitions. The first one has been done for

atom economy (efficiency)	exposure or vulnerability to injury
fertiliser	the amount of starting materials that end up as useful products
hazard	the amount of substance that contains as many elementary units as there are atoms in 12 g of carbon-12
mole	the formation of chemical compounds from more simple substances
rate of a reaction	the rate of disappearance of reactant or the rate of appearance of a product (efficiency)
relative atomic mass .	the number of times an atom is heavier than one twelfth of a carbon-12
synthesis	chemicals that provide plants with essential chemical elements

[6]

6. (a) Use either the word **fast** or **slow** to describe the rate of the following reactions:

(i) the decomposition of hydrogen peroxide using a catalyst

(ii) the reaction between potassium and water

(iii) the rusting of the steel body of a car **[3]**

(b) Name the gas formed and the catalyst used in **(a) (i)** **[1]**

7. The graphs show how the relative rates of a reaction catalysed by an enzyme varies with pH and temperature.

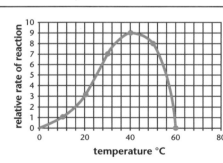 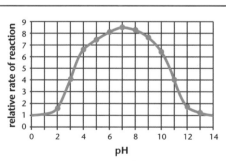

(a) Explain the shapes of both graphs. **[4]**

(b) What would be the ideal conditions of temperature and pH to get the fastest rate of reaction? **[2]**

Exam practice questions

8. A few crystals of iodine were placed in a U tube and chlorine gas passed through the tube. The tube got warm and a brown liquid, iodine monochloride (ICl) was formed. This experiment must be carried out in a fume cupboard.

(a)　**(i)** Why was the experiment carried out in a fume cupboard.

　　(ii) What evidence is there that a chemical reaction took place between the iodine and chlorine?

　　(iii) Write the equation for the formation of iodine monochloride.　**[4]**

The experiment was continued further as shown in the following sequence of diagrams.

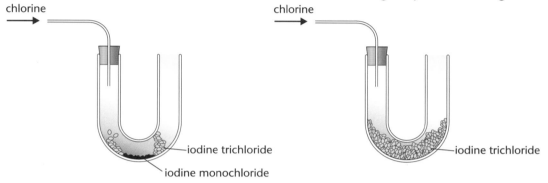

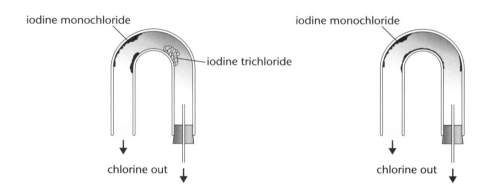

(b)　**(i)** What conclusions can be made from this experiment?

　　(ii) Write the equation for any reactions that occur.　**[2]**

Exam practice questions

9. The flow diagram below outlines the manufacture of nitric acid.

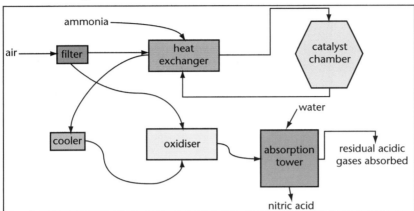

The reactions and conditions for each stage are place are:

1. Catalyst chamber
ammonia + oxygen → nitrogen monoxide + water
$4NH_3$ + $5O_2$ → $4NO$ + $6H_2O$
Conditions: platinum/rhodium gauze catalyst, excess oxygen and 300°C
The reaction is very exothermic.

2. Heat exchanger and cooler
nitrogen monoxide + oxygen → nitrogen dioxide
$2NO$ + O_2 → $2NO_2$
Conditions: 250°C

3. Absorption tower
nitrogen dioxide + water + oxygen → nitric acid
$4NO_2$ + $2H_2O$ + O_2 → $4HNO_3$
Conditions: room temperature

The overall reaction is:
ammonia + oxygen → nitric acid + water
NH_3 + $2O_2$ → HNO_3 + H_2O

(a) Why is
(i) the air filtered?
(ii) the catalyst in the form of gauze?
(iii) excess oxygen used?
(iv) a heat exchanger used? **[4]**
(b) **(i)** What are the raw materials for the manufacture of nitric acid?
(ii) What is the atom economy (efficiency) of this manufacturing process? **[4]**
(c) Identify any hazards in this manufacturing process. **[3]**
(d) If the percentage yield of this process is 60%, what mass of nitric acid can be obtained when 14 400 dm³ of ammonia is reacted with excess oxygen at room temperature and pressure? **[2]**
(e) Is the manufacture of nitric acid a batch or a continuous process?
Give reasons for your answer. **[1]**

Acids, bases, salts and electrolysis

The following topics are covered in this chapter:

- *Acids, bases and salts*
- *Salts*
- *Alkalis*

8.1 Acids, bases and salts

pH scale

OCR A	C6.1
OCR B	C4a
AQA	2.12.6

> *The colour changes of universal indicator paper are those of the colours in the rainbow – red orange yellow green blue indigo violet.*

The pH scale is a numerical scale which is used to measure the acidity or alkalinity of a solution. The scale ranges from 0 to 14. pH can be measured using indicators or a pH meter.

The colour changes using universal indicator papers are shown below.

pH	1, 2	3, 4	5, 6	7	8, 9, 10	11, 12	13, 14
colour							

Solutions with a pH of:
- less than 7, are acids
- more than 7, are alkalis
- 7, are neutral.

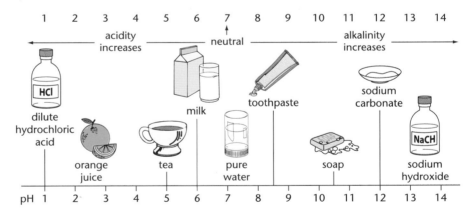

Fig. 8.1 The pH of some common substances.

Acids

OCR A	C6.1
OCR B	C4a
AQA	2.12.6
EDEXCEL 360	C1a

> *Acids only show acidic properties when they are dissolved in water.*

KEY POINT

Acids:
- **are compounds containing hydrogen that can be replaced by a metal**
- **dissolve in water to form hydrogen ions (H⁺)**
- **are proton donors**
- **have a pH of less than 7.**

Examples of acids are shown in the table.

Acid	Formula	Physical state when pure	Type of acid
hydrogen chloride dissolved in water (hydrochloric acid)	HCl	gas	mineral acids
sulfuric acid	H_2SO_4	liquid	
nitric acid	HNO_3	liquid	
ethanoic acid	CH_3COOH	liquid	organic acids
citric acid	complex	solid	
tartaric acid	complex	solid	

Only one hydrogen atom in ethanoic acid can be replaced by a metal to form sodium ethanoate CH_3COONa.

Hydrochloric acid, sulfuric acid and nitric acid are called mineral acids because they can be obtained from minerals.

Properties of acids

Although there are a large number of acids, there are several properties they have in common.

1 Taste

Acids have a sour taste.

2 Aqueous solution

Acids dissolve in water to form solutions which conduct electricity. Some acids completely ionise when they dissolve in water. These are called strong acids. The mineral acids are strong acids, e.g. sulfuric acid.

$H_2SO_4 + water \rightarrow 2H^+ + SO_4^{2-}$

Organic acids only ionise slightly when they dissolve in water. Some of the molecules remain unionised. They are called weak acids.

$CH_3COOH + water \rightleftharpoons CH_3COO^- + H^+$

In dilute ethanoic acid, about four molecules in every thousand are ionised.

3 Indicators

Acids change the colour of indicators, e.g. blue litmus turns red.

4 Fairly reactive metals

Dilute acids react with fairly reactive metals to form hydrogen

a metal	+	dilute acid	$\rightarrow$	salt	+	hydrogen
magnesium	+	dilute sulfuric acid	$\rightarrow$	magnesium sulfate	+	hydrogen
Mg	+	H_2SO_4	$\rightarrow$	$MgSO_4$	+	H_2
Mg	+	$2H^+$	$\rightarrow$	Mg^{2+}	+	H_2
zinc	+	dilute hydrochloric acid	$\rightarrow$	zinc chloride	+	hydrogen
Zn	+	2HCl	$\rightarrow$	$ZnCl_2$	+	H_2
Zn	+	$2H^+$	$\rightarrow$	Zn^{2+}	+	H_2

Magnesium sulfate and zinc chloride are **salts**.

Salts are named according to the metal ion or ammonium ion they contain and the acid from which they are made.

> **Ethanoic acid contains four hydrogen atoms per molecule, but it is a monobasic acid because only one hydrogen can be replaced.**

> **Do not taste chemicals unless you have been given permission to taste them by your teacher.**

> **Strong acids have a pH of 0, 1 or 2; weak acids have a pH of 3, 4, 5 or 6.**

Nitric acid is an exception. It does react with metals but it does not give hydrogen. Instead a nitrate, water and oxides of nitrogen are formed.

The table below shows some examples of salts from different acids.

KEY POINT A salt is a compound obtained when the hydrogen of an acid is partly or completely replaced by a metal ion or an ammonium ion, NH_4^+ .

Acid	Examples of salts	Formula
hydrochloric acid (HCl)	sodium chloride	NaCl
	magnesium chloride	$MgCl_2$
sulfuric acid (H_2SO_4)	sodium sulfate	Na_2SO_4
	zinc sulfate	$ZnSO_4$
nitric acid (HNO_3)	potassium nitrate	KNO_3
	copper(II) nitrate	$Cu(NO_3)_2$
ethanoic acid (CH_3COOH)	sodium ethanoate	CH_3COONa
	calcium ethanoate	$(CH_3COO)_2Ca$

All salts that contain oxygen have an -ate ending. Salts made up of two elements have -ide endings.

5 Metal carbonates

KEY POINT Acids react with carbonates (or hydrogencarbonates) to form a salt, carbon dioxide and water.

If a substance gives carbon dioxide with an acid it must be a carbonate (or hydrogencarbonate).

carbonate + acid → salt + water + carbon dioxide

calcium carbonate + hydrochloric acid → calcium chloride + water + carbon dioxide

$$CaCO_3 + 2HCl → CaCl_2 + H_2O + CO_2$$
$$CO_3^{2-} + 2H^+ → H_2O + CO_2$$

6 Metal oxides

Metal oxides are called bases.

KEY POINT Acids react with metal oxides to form a salt and water **only**.

metal oxide + acid → salt + water

zinc oxide + sulfuric acid → zinc sulfate + water

$$ZnO + H_2SO_4 → ZnSO_4 + H_2O$$
$$O^{2-} + 2H^+ → H_2O$$

7 Metal hydroxides

Metal hydroxides that dissolve in water are called alkalis.

KEY POINT Acids react with alkalis to form a salt and water **only**.

This reaction is known as a neutralisation reaction. Hydrogen ions from the acid react with hydroxide ions from the alkali to make water.

alkali + acid → salt + water

sodium hydroxide + hydrochloric acid → sodium chloride + water

$$NaOH + HCl → NaCl + H_2O$$
$$OH^- + H^+ → H_2O$$

Uses of acids

Over 160 million tonnes of sulfuric acid are produced worldwide in a year.

Sulfuric acid is the acid used in car batteries and to clean metal surfaces. Sulfuric acid is used to manufacture detergents, fertilisers, soaps, dyes, fibres, plastics and paints.

About 80% of the nitric acid manufactured is used for making fertilisers.

Hydrochloric acid is mainly used for cleaning metals bricks and tiles. It is also used in the manufacture of sugar and glue.

Ethanoic acid is one of the world's most important chemicals. It is used in the production of a vast range of products particularly the manufacture of PVA (polyvinyl alcohol) and adhesives.

8.2 Alkalis

Properties of alkalis

 OCR A   C6.1
 OCR B   C4a
AQA   2.12.6

> **KEY POINT**
> An alkali is a soluble base. Alkalis contain an excess of OH^- ions and have a pH greater than 7.

1 Aqueous solution

Alkalis form solutions that conduct electricity. Some alkalis dissociate completely when they dissolve in water. These are called strong alkalis. Sodium hydroxide and potassium hydroxide are strong alkalis.

$$NaOH \rightarrow Na^+ + OH^-$$

A solution of ammonia in water is a weak alkali.

Lime water, calcium hydroxide ($Ca(OH)_2$) is an alkali.

$$NH_3 + H_2O \rightarrow NH_4^+ + OH^-$$

2 Indicators

Alkalis change the colour of indicators, e.g. red litmus turns blue.

3 Reaction with acids

Alkalis neutralise acids to form salts and water.
potassium hydroxide + nitric acid → potassium nitrate + water

$$KOH + HNO_3 \rightarrow KNO_3 + H_2O$$

$$OH^- + H^+ \rightarrow H_2O$$

4 Reaction with ammonium salts

They react with ammonium salts to form ammonia.

ammonium chloride	+	sodium hydroxide	→	ammonia	+	sodium chloride	+	water
NH_4Cl	+	$NaOH$	→	NH_3	+	$NaCl$	+	H_2O

Uses of alkalis

Sodium hydroxide is economically important. It is used in the manufacture of:

- aluminium
- detergents and soaps
- fibres and paper.

8.3 Salts

Preparing soluble salts

 OCR A   C6.1
 OCR B   C 4a
  AQA   2.12.6

> **KEY POINT**
>
> There are five methods of preparing soluble salts:
>
> **acid + metal**
>
> magnesium   + hydrochloric acid   → magnesium chloride   +   hydrogen
> Mg   +   2HCl   → $MgCl_2$ + H_2
>
> **acid + metal oxide**
>
> copper(II) oxide +   sulfuric acid   →   copper(II) sulfate   +   water
> CuO   + H_2SO_4 → $CuSO_4$ + H_2O
>
> **acid + metal hydroxide**
>
> nitric acid   + lead(II) hydroxide   →   lead(II) nitrate   +   water
> $2HNO_3$ + $Pb(OH)_2$ → $Pb(NO_3)_2$ + H_2O
>
> **acid + carbonate**
>
> hydrochloric acid + barium carbonate →   barium chloride   +   water   +   carbon dioxide
> 2HCl   + $BaCO_3$ → $BaCl_2$ + H_2O + CO_2

> **The method used depends upon factors such as speed of reaction, availability of chemicals and cost.**

The method of preparation is the same in each case. The method is summarised in Fig. 8.1.

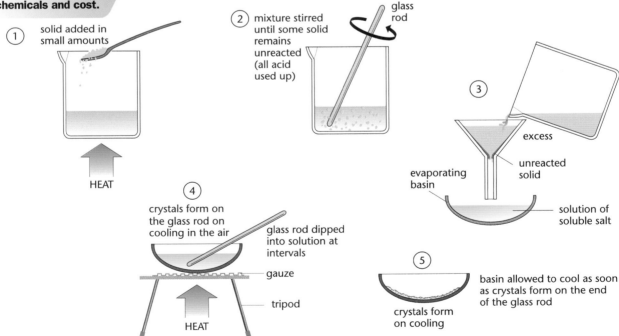

Fig. 8.1 How to prepare a salt.

acid + alkali

hydrochloric acid + sodium hydroxide → sodium chloride + water

HCl + $NaOH$ → $NaCl$ + H_2O

This reaction is known as neutralisation.

An alkali is a metal oxide or metal hydroxide that is soluble in water.

KEY POINT — **A neutralisation reaction is a reaction between an acid and an alkali, in the correct proportions to produce a neutral salt.**

A titration method is used if the hydroxide is an alkali such as potassium hydroxide (KOH), sodium hydroxide (NaOH) or ammonia solution (NH_3(aq)).

The nitric acid is placed in a beaker using a pipette. Sodium hydroxide solution is added from the burette. An indicator such as litmus, phenolphthalein or methyl orange is used to detect the end-point.

The solution is evaporated to crystallisation point, cooled and filtered. The crystals are washed and then dried between pieces of filter paper.

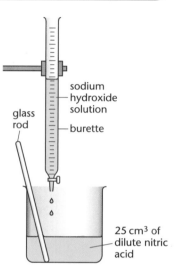

Fig. 8.3 Preparing a salt using titration method.

Preparation of fertilisers

The reaction taking place in the above reaction is:

nitric acid + potassium hydroxide → potassium nitrate + water

HNO_3 + KOH → KNO_3 + H_2O

Potassium nitrate is used as a fertiliser. This method can also be used for making the fertiliser ammonium nitrate, ammonium sulfate and ammonium phosphate.

nitric acid + ammonia solution → ammonium nitrate

HNO_3 + NH_3 → NH_4NO_3

sulfuric acid + ammonia solution → ammonium sulfate

H_2SO_4 + $2NH_3$ → $(NH_4)_2SO_4$

phosphoric acid + ammonia solution → ammonium phosphate

H_3PO_4 + $3NH_3$ → $(NH_4)_3PO_4$

Other salts can be made by neutralisation.

Salt	Use
lithium chloride	crimson colour in fireworks
lead(II) chromate(VI)	yellow colouring agent in paint
potassium chlorate(VI)	combustion of fuels, it is a powerful oxidising agent

pH changes during titrations

Fig. 8.2 shows how the pH of the mixture varies as sodium hydroxide is added until it is present in excess.

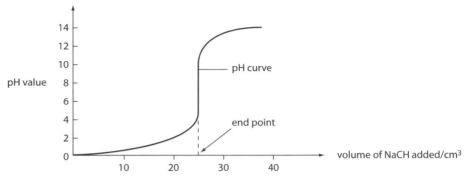

Fig. 8.2 Changes in pH value during an acid-base titration.

> The pH would decrease if excess acid was added to an alkali.

Note that the pH increases as alkali is added:

The H^+ ions react with the OH^- to form water,

$$H^+ + OH^- \rightarrow H_2O$$

Preparation of an insoluble salt

> **KEY POINT**
>
> **Insoluble salts are made by the process of precipitation.**

Two solutions each containing half the salt to be prepared are mixed together. The salt is then precipitated.

Lead(II) carbonate can be prepared by mixing together lead(II) nitrate solution and sodium carbonate solution.

> Common insoluble salts include silver chloride, barium sulfate and most carbonates (except carbonates of sodium, potassium and ammonium).

lead(II) nitrate + sodium carbonate → lead(II) carbonate + sodium nitrate
$$Pb(NO_3)_2 \quad + \quad Na_2CO_3 \quad \rightarrow \quad PbCO_3 \quad + \quad 2NaNO_3$$

In order to get a pure sample of lead(II) carbonate the mixture is filtered, washed with distilled water and dried.

> **KEY POINT**
>
> **This type of reaction is sometimes called double decomposition and is represented by the equation: AX + BY → AY + BX.**

Electrolysis

OCR A	C5.4
OCR B	C3f
AQA	2.12.6
EDEXCEL 360	C2.6

> **KEY POINT**
>
> **Electrolysis is an important process. It was developed by Michael Faraday in the early nineteenth century when suitable supplies of electricity became available. He discovered a number of new elements including the group 1 and group 2 metals.**

Metals and graphite conduct electricity but they are not electrolytes because they do not decompose.

> **KEY POINT**
> An electrolyte is a molten ionic compound or an aqueous solution that conducts electricity.

- Solid electrolytes do not conduct electricity.
- When electrolytes are molten or dissolved in water, the ions present become 'free' to move.
- The 'free' ions allow electricity to flow.
- Acids, alkalis and salts are electrolytes.

> **KEY POINT**
> Electrolysis is the process of using electricity to break down or decompose a compound.

Explaining electrolysis

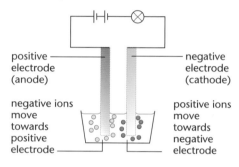

Fig. 8.5 Movement of ions during electrolysis.

- In the external circuit, electrons flow from the positive electrode (anode) to the negative electrode (cathode) of the battery.

Oxidation is loss of electrons.

- During electrolysis, the negative ions (anions) travel to the anode where they give up electrons to the anode (oxidation).

Reduction is gain of electrons.

- During electrolysis, the positive ions (cations) travel to the cathode where they receive electrons from the cathode (reduction).

Metals and hydrogen form positive ions (cations) and so they move to the negative electrode (cathode) during electrolysis.

Non-metals form negative ions (anions) and so they move to the positive electrode (anode) during electrolysis.

Both electrodes are usually made of graphite because it:
- conducts electricity
- has a high melting point.

Electrolysis of aqueous solutions

In pure water, about 1 in every 600 000 000 water molecules ionises into hydrogen ions and hydroxide ions.

The very small ionisation explains why water is such a poor conductor of electricity.

$$H_2O \rightleftharpoons H^+ + OH^-$$

The apparatus shown in Fig. 8.6 can be used for the electrolysis of aqueous electrolytes.

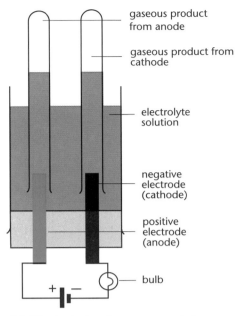

Fig. 8.6 Electrolysis of aqueous solutions.

Which ions are discharged?

Providing the concentration of the ions in solution are approximately the same, the order of discharge is:

Cathode	Anode	
silver ions Ag^{2+}	hydroxide ion OH^-	
copper ions Cu^{2+}	iodide ion I^-	ease of discharge
hydrogen ions H^+	bromide ion Br^-	decreases
lead ions Pb^{2+}	chloride ion Cl^-	
iron ions Fe^{2+}	nitrate ion NO_3^-	
	sulfate ion SO_4^{2-}	

Rules for predicting the ions discharged

Rule	
1	Identify the ions present in the electrolyte. Remember that aqueous solutions contain $H^+(aq)$ and $OH^-(aq)$ ions from water.
2	**At the anode** The product is always oxygen unless the solution contains I^-, Br^- or Cl^-
3	**At the cathode** If the cations are from metals above hydrogen in the reactivity series, then hydrogen will be formed. If the cations are from metals below hydrogen in the reactivity series, then the metal will be formed.
4	Identify the cations and anions left in the solution. They form the product that remains after the electrolysis.

Electrolysis of dilute sulfuric acid

The ions present in solution are:

H^+ and SO_4^{2-} from the sulfuric acid

$H^+ + OH^-$ from water (See rule 1).

> The reaction at the cathode is reduction – gain of electrons.

At the cathode

H^+ ions travel to the cathode and are discharged (see rule 2)

$2H^+ + 2e \rightarrow H_2$

The reaction at the anode is oxidation – loss of electrons.

At the anode

OH^- ions and SO_4^{2-} ions travel to the anode

OH^- ions are discharged in preference to SO_4^{2-} ions (see rule 3)

$4OH^- - 4e \rightarrow 2H_2O + O_2$

During the electrolysis of dilute sulfuric acid **HYDROGEN is given off at the cathode** and **OXYGEN is given off at the anode**. The concentration of the sulfuric acid increases.

Remember the tests for these two gases – hydrogen burns with a 'pop' and oxygen relights a glowing splint.

The ions left in solution are H^+ and SO_4^{2-}. The sulfuric acid becomes more concentrated. (see rule 4).

Electrolysis of concentrated sodium chloride (brine)

The ions present in solution are:

Na^+ and Cl^- from the sodium chloride

$H^+ + OH^-$ from water (see rule 1)

At the cathode

H^+ ions and Na^+ ions travel to the cathode

H^+ ions are discharge in preference to Na^+ ions (see rule 3)

$2H^+ + 2e \rightarrow H_2$

At the anode

OH^- ions and Cl^- ions travel to the anode

Cl^- ions are discharged in preference to OH^- ions (see rule 2)

$2Cl^- - 2e \rightarrow Cl_2$

During the electrolysis of concentrated sodium chloride **HYDROGEN is given off at the cathode** and **CHLORINE is given off at the anode**. The Na^+ ions combine with the OH^- ions to form sodium hydroxide (see rule 4).

The electrolysis of brine is used to manufacture chlorine, sodium hydroxide and hydrogen.

- Chlorine is used to sterilise water and to make solvents, household bleach and plastics.
- Hydrogen is used in the manufacture of margarine.
- Sodium hydroxide is used in the manufacture of soap.

Electrolysis of dilute sodium chloride

When molten sodium chloride is electrolysed, sodium is formed at the cathode and chlorine at the anode.

The ions present in solution are:

Na^+ and Cl^- from the sodium chloride

$H^+ + OH^-$ from water (see rule 1)

At the cathode

H^+ ions and Na^+ ions travel to the cathode

H^+ ions are discharge in preference to Na^+ ions (see rule 3)

$2H^+ + 2e \rightarrow H_2$

At the anode

OH^- ions and Cl^- ions travel to the anode

OH^- ions are discharged in preference to Cl^- ions (see rule 2)

$4OH^- - 4e \rightarrow 2H_2O + O_2$

During the electrolysis of dilute sodium chloride **HYDROGEN is given off at the cathode** and **OXYGEN is given off at the anode**. The Na^+ ions combine with the Cl^- ions to form sodium chloride (see rule 4).

The sodium chloride gets more concentrated – eventually the chloride ion concentration will be large enough for chlorine to be discharged instead of oxygen.

Products of electrolysis of various aqueous electrolytes using inert electrodes

The table below shows what happens when other electrolytes are electrolysed.

Aqueous electrolyte	Product at		Effect on solution
	cathode	anode	
dilute hydrochloric acid	hydrogen	oxygen	hydrochloric acid gets more concentrated
concentrated hydrochloric acid	hydrogen	chlorine	hydrochloric acid gets more dilute
copper(II) sulfate	copper	oxygen	sulfuric acid formed
concentrated copper(II) chloride	copper	chlorine	solution gets paler as the solution gets more dilute
aqueous potassium nitrate solution	hydrogen	oxygen	aqueous potassium nitrate solution gets more concentrated
aqueous potassium sulfate solution	hydrogen	oxygen	aqueous potassium sulfate solution gets more concentrated
aqueous silver nitrate solution	silver	oxygen	nitric acid formed

Extraction of aluminium

We have seen that aluminium is extracted by electrolysis. Purified bauxite (aluminium oxide (Al_2O_3)) is dissolved in molten sodium aluminium fluoride (cryolite (Na_3AlF_6)) to form a mixture which has a relatively low melting point. The method used in shown Fig. 8.7.

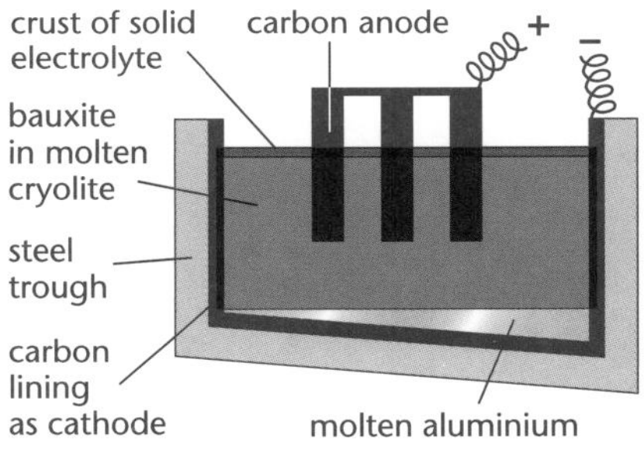

The electrodes are made of carbon.

Fig. 8.7 Extraction of aluminium.

The reactions taking place are:

● at the cathode: $Al^{3+} + 3e^- \rightarrow Al$
● at the anode: $2O^{2-} \rightarrow O_2 + 4e^-$

The aluminium sinks to the bottom of the cell where it is siphoned off.

The anode slowly burns away as the carbon reacts with oxygen to form carbon dioxide.

Don't forget to recycle your drinks cans.

The cost of manufacture of aluminium from its ore is high. Recycled aluminium uses only about 5% of the energy required to extract it from bauxite.

Use of aluminium	Reason for use
aircraft, ships, trains, cars	low density, strong, does not corrode
drinking cans	low density, strong, does not corrode
overhead power cables (with a steel core to strengthen them)	low density, does not corrode, good conductor of electricity
saucepans	low density, resists corrosion, good appearance, good conductor of heat

Copper

OCR B   C2d
AQA   12.6

Copper has properties that make it useful for electrical wiring and plumbing.

Pure copper is more economically viable than impure copper because it is a better conductor. Pure copper is a good conductor of electricity. Copper is purified by electrolysis using the cell shown in Fig. 8.8.

Pure copper is used as the cathode, impure copper as the anode and copper(II) sulfate as the electrolyte.

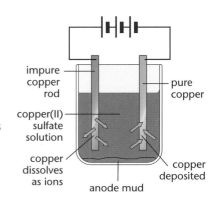

Fig. 8.8 How copper is purified.

> **KEY POINT** During electrolysis, copper from the anode goes into solution as copper ions. Copper ions from the copper(II) sulfate are deposited on the cathode.

The changes taking place are:
At the anode $Cu \rightarrow Cu^{2+} + 2e^-$
At the cathode $Cu^{2+} + 2e^- \rightarrow Cu$

Impurities in the copper collect under the copper anode.

The supply of copper-rich ores is limited. New ways of extracting copper from low-grade ores are being researched to limit the environmental impact of traditional mining. Most of the copper we buy nowadays has been recycled from old copper wires and pipes.

> **The impurities contain valuable metals such as silver and gold.**

Extraction of metals can have an impact on the environment.

● The mined land is unsightly and creates an area which cannot support plant life and animal life.
● It causes problems including where and how to dispose of the waste.
● It uses vast amounts of energy.

Some of the waste products cause air pollution.

HOW SCIENCE WORKS

An everyday acid

Ascorbic acid, also known as vitamin C, has the structure shown in the diagram.

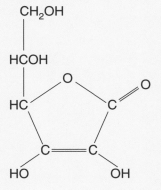

It is a white crystalline solid that is soluble is water. It is destroyed by heat and light.

Humans, and a few other species including guinea pigs, cannot synthesise ascorbic acid and must obtain it in their food.

Ascorbic acid can be produced commercially by:
- extraction from plants
- chemical synthesis
- fermentation of sorbitol ($C_6H_{14}O_6$) followed by oxidation.

The amount in foods of plant origin depends on the:
- variety of the plant
- soil condition
- climate in which it grew
- length of time since it was picked
- storage conditions
- method of preparation.

The table below shows the vitamin C content of broccoli from a variety of sources.

Source	Amount (mg/100 g)	Source	Amount (mg/100 g)	Source	Amount (mg/100 g)	Source	Amount (mg/100 g)
fresh broccoli	90	frozen broccoli	85	supermarket broccoli	60	cooked broccoli	40

The concentration of a solution of ascorbic acid can be determined by titration with an oxidising agent. One of the oxidising agents used is the dye 2,6-dichlorophenol-indophenol, or DCPIP for short. The titration must be performed quickly because there are usually other reducing agents present that react more slowly with DCPIP.

To find the amount of vitamin C in 100 g of Brussels sprouts using DCPIP

25 g of Brussels sprouts is pounded with 100 cm^3 of water and the mixture filtered. 5 cm^3 of the filtrate is placed in a small flask and a few crystals of oxalic acid (a poisonous compound) added and the mixture shaken. DCPIP is run into the mixture solution until the blue colour changes to a faint pink colour that lasts for 15 seconds.

1.0 cm^3 of DCPIP is equivalent to 0.1 mg of vitamin C.

Sample results for the amount of DCPIP required for 5 different experiments are 9.8 cm^3, 9.6 cm^3; 9.7 cm^3, 9.4 cm^3 and 9.6 cm^3.

HOW SCIENCE WORKS

To find the amount of vitamin C in a vitamin C tablet using iodine solution

The tablet is finely ground into a powder and dissolved in about $80\,cm^3$ of water. About $10\,cm^3$ of concentrated hydrochloric acid is added and shaken vigorously. A few drops of starch solution are added as an indicator. (Starch solution turns blue/black in the presence of iodine.)

$0.05\,mol/dm^3$ solution of iodine is added from a burette until the solution becomes permanently blue/black.

$1\,cm^3$ of the iodine solution is equivalent to $8.81\,mg$ of vitamin C.

Sample results for the amount of iodine solution required for 5 different experiments are $28.0\,cm^3$; $27.2\,cm^3$; $24.4\,cm^3$; $30.3\,cm^3$; and $26.5\,cm^3$.

HOW SCIENCE WORKS
Questions

DCPIP titration

1. What precautions must you take when carrying out the DCPIP titration? **[4]**
2. Suggestion with reasons, which titration was performed last? **[2]**
3. Calculate a value for the amount of vitamin C in 100 g of Brussels sprouts. Show your working. **[4]**

Iodine titration

4. Which of the following is the strength of the tablets?
   25 mg, 50 mg; 100 mg; 250 mg or 500 mg. Show your working. **[2]**
5. Suggest why iodine solution was not used to measure the vitamin C content in Brussels sprouts **[2]**

Vitamin C

6. What is:
   (a) the molecular formula of ascorbic acid
   (b) the empirical formula of ascorbic acid? **[2]**
7. What effect does each of the following have on the vitamin C content of vegetables?
   (a) boiling
   (b) leaving uneaten for several days
   (c) freezing
   (d) leaving to stand in water **[4]**
8. Explain, with reasons, whether ascorbic acid is a typical:
   (a) carboxylic acid
   (b) vitamin. **[2]**

Exam practice questions

1. In an experiment to find the composition of an indigestion tablet, each of five students performed the following experiment:
    *   one tablet was dissolved in 100 cm³ of water
    *   using a pipette, 25.0 cm³ of the solution were placed in a conical flask and titrated against dilute hydrochloric acid, using methyl orange as the indicator.

    The results of the 5 students were:

Student	1	2	3	4	5
Volume of hydrochloric acid used/cm³	21.2	21.3	23.1	21.2	21.2

    Which statement explains the result of student 3?
    A   The burette was washed out with the tablet solution.
    B   The conical flask was washed out with the tablet solution
    C   The pipette was washed out with the tablet solution.
    D   The student measured to the top of the meniscus in the burette.   **[1]**

2. The diagram shows stages in the manufacture of the fertiliser ammonium sulfate.
    At which stage, **A**, **B**, **C** or **D**, would a leak in the manufacturing process give the largest increase in the pH of rain?

    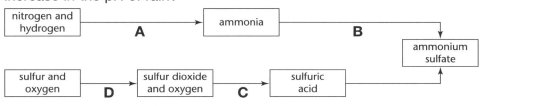

    [1]

3. Some heat reflecting shields on space shuttles are gold-plated. The shields are first coated in graphite to provide a conducting surface before the shields are gold-plated using electrolysis.
    Which electrodes would be used in a soluble gold electrolyte to plate the shields?

	Negative electrode	**Positive electrode**
A	carbon	heat shield
B	gold	heat shield
C	heat shield	carbon
D	heat shield	gold

    [1]

4. Choose words from the list below to fill in the gaps in the passage

    acid   carbon dioxide   hydrogen   hydrated   anhydrous
    metallic   precipitation   sodium   sulfuric   water

    All salts are ___**ionic**___ compounds. A salt is formed when a ____**1**____ ion or
    an ammonium ion replaces one or more ____**2**____ Ions of an ____**3**____.
    Salts that contain water of crystallisation are called ____**4**____ salts. Salts that
    DO NOT contain water of crystallisation are called ____**5**____ anhydrous salts.
    Zinc sulfate can be made by reacting zinc carbonate with ____**6**____ acid. The
    gas given off is ____**7**____. Also formed in this reaction is ____**8**____.
    All ____**9**____ salts are soluble in water. Insoluble salts are usually
    prepared by ____**10**____.   **[10]**

Exam practice questions

5. Match each of the following terms with their definitions. The first one has been done for you.

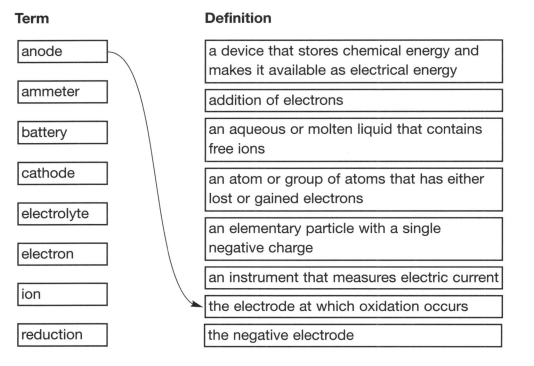

Term	Definition
anode	a device that stores chemical energy and makes it available as electrical energy
ammeter	addition of electrons
battery	an aqueous or molten liquid that contains free ions
cathode	an atom or group of atoms that has either lost or gained electrons
electrolyte	an elementary particle with a single negative charge
electron	an instrument that measures electric current
ion	the electrode at which oxidation occurs
reduction	the negative electrode

[7]

6. The pH of the saliva in Emily's mouth was 6.9. She then ate an apple and the pH of her saliva was measured every 5 minutes for 50 minutes.

time/min	0	5	10	15	20	25	30	35	40	45	50
pH	6.9	5.5	4.7	4.2	4.5	5.4	6.3	6.6	6.8	6.9	6.9

(a) (i) Plot the above results on a graph.

   (ii) Draw a smooth curve through the points. [5]

(b) From your graph determine:

   (i) the minimum pH reached by the saliva

   (ii) the time taken for the saliva to return to the original pH. [2]

(c) (i) What type of compound must be present in the apple?

   (ii) Briefly outline how the pH of apple juice could be measured. [2]

7. A group of students were divided into groups and asked to say what they thought an acid was. State, giving your reasons and examples, whether or not you agree with the definitions.

	Definition of acid
Group 1	A substance that reacts with metals to form hydrogen is an acid
Group 2	Acids are substances with a bitter taste
Group 3	An acid gives a proton to a base
Group 4	An acid increases the H+ ion concentration in water
Group 5	An acid must contain oxygen
Group 6	Substances containing hydrogen are acids

[6]

Exam practice questions

8. Using the information below place the following species in the Venn diagram.

Br^- HBr H_2O HCO_3^- H_3O^+
Na^+ NH_3 NH_4^+ OH^-

(a) Sodium bromide dissolves in water to give a solution with a pH of 7
$NaBr \rightarrow Na^+ + Br^-$

(b) Hydrogen chloride dissolves in water to give a solution with a pH of 1
$HCl + \rightarrow H^+ + Cl^-$

(c) Ammonia dissolves in water to give a solution with a pH of 11
$NH_3 + H_2O \rightarrow NH_4^+ + OH^-$

(d) Carbon dioxide dissolves in water to give a solution with a pH of 5. There are two reactions that take place
$CO_2 + H_2O \rightarrow H^+ + HCO_3^-$
$HCO_3^- \rightarrow H^+ + CO_3^{2-}$

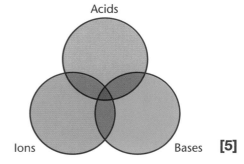

Acids

Ions   Bases   **[5]**

9. The diagram below was used to electrolyse various aqueous solutions using the same conditions for each experiment. The volume of gas collected in syringe A for the first experiment was $80\,cm^3$.

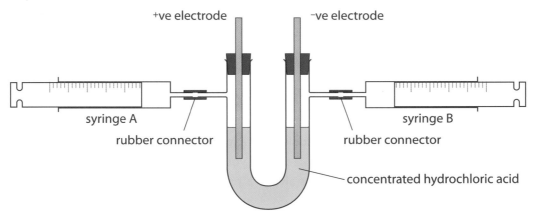

+ve electrode   −ve electrode

syringe A   syringe B

rubber connector   rubber connector

concentrated hydrochloric acid

Experiment 1 Concentrated hydrochloric acid using carbon electrodes
(a) Name the gas that is collected in syringe A. **[1]**
(b) Explain why the volume of chlorine collected in syringe B is less than $80\,cm^3$ **[1]**
(c) Explain why the electrodes are made of carbon and not of a metal such as iron. **[2]**

Experiment 2 Dilute sulfuric acid using platinum electrodes
(d) Write the formulae of all the ions present in dilute sulfuric acid. **[3]**
(e) Name the gas that is collected in **(i)** syringe A and **(ii)** syringe B. **[2]**
(f) Write the equations for the formation of the gases formed in **(e)(i)** and **(e)(ii)**. **[2]**
(g) What volume of gas will be formed in syringe B? **[1]**

Experiment 3 Calcium hydroxide solution using carbon electrodes
(h) Explain why a white precipitate is formed in the U-tube. Write equations for any reactions taking place. **[6]**

Forces and motion

The following topics are covered in this chapter:

- **Speed, velocity and acceleration**
- **Momentum and collisions**
- **Forces and their effects**
- **Work, energy and power**

9.1 Speed, velocity and acceleration

Speed and distance-time graphs

 OCR A   C4.1.1
 OCR B   P3a
AQA   P2.13.1

Speed is measured in metres per second (m/s) or kilometres per hour (km/h). If an athlete runs with a **speed** of 5 m/s, she will cover 5 metres in one second and 10 metres in two seconds. An athlete with a faster speed of 8 m/s will travel further, 8 m in each second, and will take less time to complete his journey.

> *For how to rearrange the formula see page 223.*

 KEY POINT

To calculate speed:

$$\text{speed (m/s)} = \frac{\text{distance (m)}}{\text{time (s)}}$$

Direction of travel

 OCR A   P4.1
AQA   P2.13.1
EDEXCEL 360   P2.9

There are two ways of looking at a journey:
- You can say that the **distance** you travel can only increase or stay the same, and then the **speed** is always a positive number.
- You can consider the **direction** you travel, so that if you travel towards school, that is a **positive** distance and when you travel in the opposite direction that is a **negative** distance. Sometimes, distance in a given direction is called **displacement**.

> *You only need to know the term 'displacement' for Edexcel.*

Quantities that have a **magnitude** and **direction** are called **vectors**.

Velocity is a **vector**, because velocity is speed in a given direction.

Example A boy walks in a positive direction and then back again with a constant **speed** of 2 m/s, so he walks with a **velocity** of +2 m/s and then with a velocity of –2m/s.

> *For how to rearrange the formula see page 223.*

$$\text{velocity (m/s)} = \frac{\text{displacement (m)}}{\text{time (s)}}$$

Distance–time graphs

OCR A   P4.1
OCR B   P3a
AQA   P2.13.1

On a **distance–time graph**:
- a **horizontal line** means the object is **stopped**
- a **straight line sloping upwards** means it has a **steady speed**.

The steepness, or **gradient**, of the line shows the speed:
- a **steeper gradient** means a **higher speed**
- a **curved line** means the **speed is changing**.

If the direction of travel is being considered:
- A negative distance is in the opposite direction to a positive distance.
- A **straight line sloping downwards** means it has a **steady speed**, and a **steady velocity** in the negative direction.

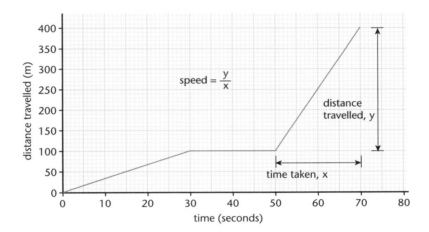

Fig. 9.1 Distance–time graph for a cycle ride.

Between 30 s and 50 s the cyclist stopped. The graph has a **steeper gradient** between 50 s and 70 s than between 0 s and 20 s – the cyclist was travelling at a **greater speed**.

To calculate a speed from a graph, work out the gradient of the straight line section as shown in Fig. 9.1:

speed = $\frac{y}{x}$ where y = 400 m – 100 m = 300 m and x = 70 s – 50 s = 20 s.

$$\text{speed} = \frac{300\,m}{20\,s} = 15\,m/s.$$

Average speed and instantaneous speed

You can calculate the **average speed** of the cyclist for the **total** journey in Fig. 9.1 using:

$$\text{average speed} = \frac{\text{total distance}}{\text{total time}}$$

$$\frac{400\,m}{70\,s} = 5.7\,m/s$$

> **This is an important point for OCR A.**

This is not the same as the **instantaneous speed** at any moment because the speed changes during the journey. If you calculate the **average speed** over a **shorter time** interval you get closer to the **instantaneous speed**.

Velocity–time and speed–time graphs

OCR A   P4.1
OCR B   P3b
AQA   P2.13.1
EDEXCEL 360   P2.9

A **change of velocity** is called **acceleration**. Speeding up, slowing down and changing direction are all examples of acceleration.

Fig. 9.2 shows how to interpret a velocity–time graph.

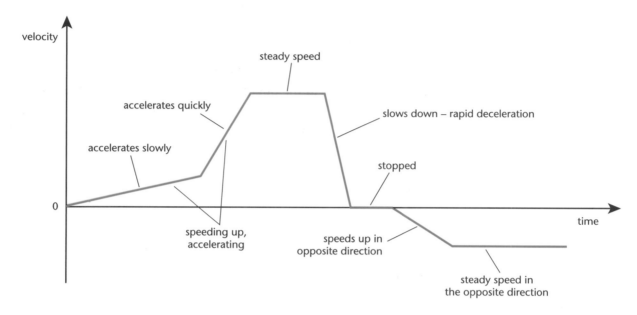

Fig. 9.2 A velocity–time graph.

- A **positive slope** (**gradient**) means that the **speed is increasing** – the object is **accelerating**.
- A **horizontal line** means that the object is travelling at a **steady speed**.

> Check carefully whether a graph is a speed-time graph or a distance-time graph.

- A **negative slope** (**gradient**) means the **speed is decreasing** – **negative acceleration**.
- A **curved slope** means that the **acceleration** is **changing** – the object has **non-uniform acceleration**.

On true **speed–time graphs**, the speed has only positive values. On **velocity–time graphs** the velocity can be negative.

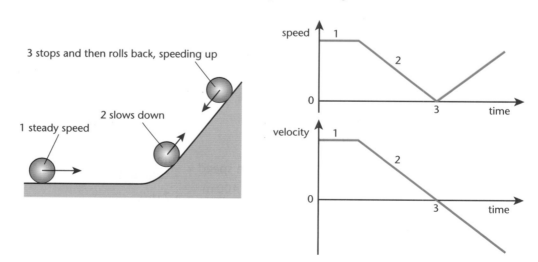

Fig. 9.3 Graphs for a ball that rolls up a hill, slows, and rolls back down, speeding up.

Tachographs are instruments that are put in lorry cabs to check that the lorry has not exceeded the speed limit, and that the driver has stopped for breaks. They draw a graph of the speed against time for the lorry.

Graphs, acceleration and distance

For how to rearrange the formula see page 223.

KEY POINT

Acceleration is the change in velocity per second:

$$\text{Acceleration (m/s}^2) = \frac{\text{change in velocity (m)}}{\text{time taken (s)}}$$

$a = \dfrac{(v - u)}{t}$ where a is the acceleration of an object whose velocity changes from u to v in time t

Fig. 9.4 is a graph of speed against time for a car journey.

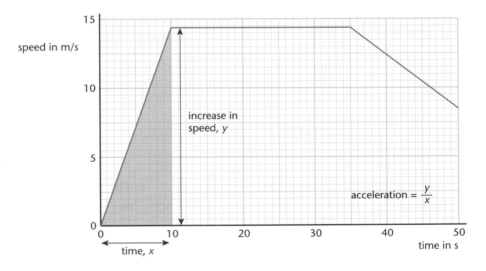

Fig 9.4 Speed–time graph for a car journey.

In the first 10 s the acceleration is: $\dfrac{(14 - 0)\,\text{m/s}}{10\,\text{s}} = 1.4\,\text{m/s}^2$

The distance travelled in the first 10 seconds is given by the shaded area.

Distance travelled = average speed × time

average speed = $\dfrac{1}{2}$ (14 − 0) m/s and time = 10 s

Distance travelled in metres = $\dfrac{1}{2}$ (14 − 0) × 10 which is the area of the shaded triangle ($\dfrac{1}{2}$ base × height).

The distance travelled in the next 25 s is represented by the rectangle.

Distance = 14 m/s × 25 s = 350 m

KEY POINT

On a speed–time graph, the area between the graph and the time axis represents the distance travelled.

9.2 Forces and their effects

Mass and weight

 OCR B — P3h
AQA — P2.13.2

Mass is measured in **kilograms**. An object has the same mass on the Earth, on the Moon, or far out in deep space. **Weight** is a **force** and is measured in **newtons**. Weight is due to **gravity** attracting the mass towards the centre of the Earth. In deep space there is no gravity and the mass has no weight. On the Moon, which has less mass than the Earth, the gravitational attraction is less, so objects will have less weight than they have on the Earth (only one sixth).

For how to rearrange the formula see page 223.

KEY POINT

weight (N) = mass (kg) x gravitational field strength (N/kg)

Gravitational field strength close to the surface of the Earth is assumed to be a constant 10 N/kg. Objects in free fall have a constant acceleration of 10 m/s².

The resultant force and balanced forces

 OCR A — P4.2, 3
AQA — P2.13.2
EDEXCEL 360 — P2.9

Forces have **size** and **direction**. On diagrams they are represented by arrows, in the **direction** the force acts. The **length** of the arrow represents the **size** of the force.

When an object has several forces acting on it, the effect is the same as one force in a certain direction. This is called the **resultant force**. Fig. 9.5 shows how forces can be combined to give a resultant force. If the **resultant force** is **zero** the forces on the object are **balanced**.

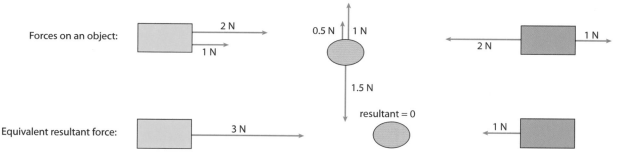

Fig. 9.5 resultant forces.

A **resultant force** is needed to change the **velocity** of an object. If the **forces** on an object are **balanced** then it will remain **stationary**, or, if it is moving, it will continue to move at a **steady speed** in the **same direction**. This seems strange because we are used to frictional forces slowing things down.

Fig. 9.6 shows how the forces on an object can be balanced so that it does not fall.

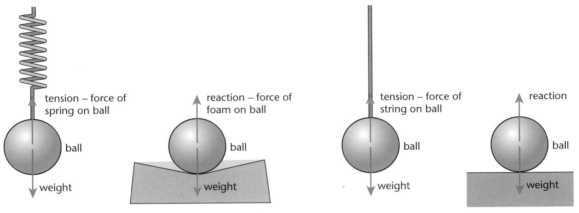

The upward force of the spring, or the foam, trying to return to their original shape balances the weight.

Even though the changes in shape are too small for us to see, the restoring force – the tension in the string or the reaction from the floor, balances the weight.

Fig 9.6 Reaction and tension are forces that can balance weight.

Resistance to motion – friction and drag

OCR A — P4.2, 3
OCR B — P3c,e,f,g
AQA — P2.13.2
EDEXCEL 360 — P2.9

When one object slides over another there is **friction**, a **resistive force** between the two surfaces. This arises because, on a microscopic scale, the surfaces are not completely smooth and the high points become stuck together.

Air resistance (or **drag**), is a **resistive force** that acts against objects that are moving through the air. **Drag** acts on objects moving through any **fluid** (gas or liquid) – and is larger in liquids.

Friction and **drag forces**:
● always act **against** the direction of motion
● are **zero** when there is **no movement**
● increase as the **speed** of the object increases.

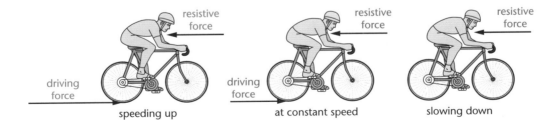

Fig 9.7 The forces on a cyclist when speeding up, at constant speed, and slowing down.

When the driving force is **larger** than the resistive force, the cyclist **speeds up**; when they are **equal** he travels at a **steady speed**, and when the driving force is less than the resistive force he **slows down**.

When an object falls it can reach a **steady speed** called **terminal velocity** where the **drag** equals the **weight**,

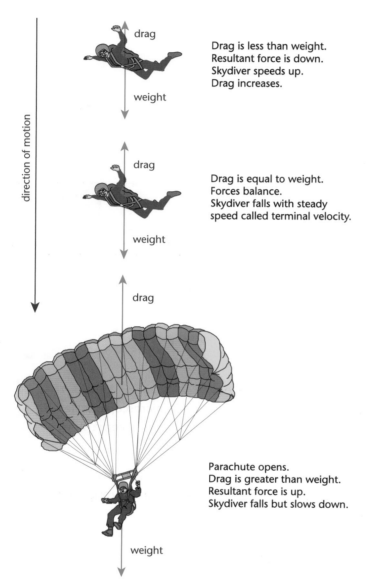

Drag is less than weight.
Resultant force is down.
Skydiver speeds up.
Drag increases.

Drag is equal to weight.
Forces balance.
Skydiver falls with steady
speed called terminal velocity.

Parachute opens.
Drag is greater than weight.
Resultant force is up.
Skydiver falls but slows down.

Fig 9.8 Forces when skydiving.

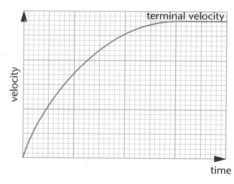

Fig 9.9 A falling object eventually reaches a terminal velocity.

Interaction pairs – action and reaction forces

OCR A | P4.2
OCR B | P3c
AQA | P2.13.2
EDEXCEL 360 | P2.9

When two objects interact, there is always an **interaction pair** of **forces**. In Fig. 9.10, skater A cannot push skater B without skater B pushing skater A.

In an **interaction pair of forces**, the two forces:

• are always **equal** in size and **opposite** in direction
• always act on **different** objects.

Fig. 9.10 when two skaters push each other, they both move backwards.

Do not confuse these forces, which act on different objects, with balanced forces, which act on the same object.

> **KEY POINT**
>
> When two objects interact, the forces they exert on each other are equal and opposite and are called action and reaction forces.

A **rocket** and a **jet engine** make use of this effect. There is an equal and opposite **reaction force** to the force of the hot exhaust gases pushed out of the back. This reaction force sends the rocket or jet forward.

Friction is the force that provides the **reaction force** you need for walking or for transport using wheels. Fig. 9.11 shows the force of **the wheel pushing back on the road** and the reaction – the friction force – of **the road pushing forward on the wheel**, which sends the wheel forward.

Imagine walking, or cycling, on a frictionless icy surface. You would slip back and never move forward.

Fig. 9.11 Forces that make a wheel move forward.

Descriptions of what is pushing/pulling on what are important in OCR A.

When you walk, **your foot pushes back on the ground** and the **ground pushes forward on your foot**.

Force and acceleration

OCR B   P3c, f
AQA   P2.13.2
EDEXCEL 360   P2.9

A **resultant force** on an object causes it to **accelerate**. The acceleration:

- is in the same **direction** as the force
- increases as the size of the **force** increases
- depends on the **mass** of the object – is smaller for a larger mass.

For how to rearrange the formula see page 223.

> **KEY POINT**
>
> For a resultant force on an object with mass m:
>
> **Force (N) = mass (kg) × acceleration (m s^{-2})** most GCSE uses m/s^2.

Stopping distances

The distance that a vehicle travels between the driver noticing a hazard and when the vehicle stops is called the **stopping distance**:

$$\text{stopping distance} = \text{thinking distance} + \text{braking distance}$$

- **Thinking distance** is the distance travelled during the driver's reaction time – the time between seeing the hazard and applying the brakes.
- **Braking distance** is the distance travelled while the vehicle is braking.

This diagram shows the shortest stopping distances at different speeds.

> **When speed doubles, thinking distance doubles, and braking distance is four times as far.**

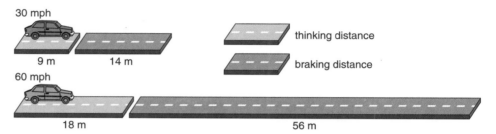

Fig. 9.12 The stopping distance increases with speed.

The **stopping distances** will also be longer if:

- The **driver** is **tired**, or affected by **drugs** (including **alcohol** and some medicines,) or **distracted** and not concentrating. Reaction time, and thinking distance are increased.
- The **road** is **wet** or **icy** or the **tyres** or **brakes** are in poor condition. The friction forces will be less, so the braking distance will increase.
- The **vehicle** is **fully loaded** with passengers or goods. The extra **mass** reduces the deceleration during braking, so the braking distance is increased.

These stopping distances are taken into account when road speed limits are set. Drivers should not drive closer than the thinking distance to the car in front, allowing them time to react. They should also reduce speed in bad weather to allow for the increased braking distance.

An anti-lock braking system (ABS) helps to keep the stopping times to a minimum. If the wheels start to slip because there is not enough friction (making the stopping distance longer), the system disconnects the brakes for a moment, the wheel grips the road, and the system reapplies the brakes.

9.3 Momentum and collisions

Momentum

For how to rearrange the formula see page 223.

OCR A · P4.3
OCR B · P5d
AQA · P2.13.4
EDEXCEL 360 · P2.9

Ten-pin bowling balls are available with different **mass**. A fast moving ball with low mass can be as effective as a slow ball with high mass. This is because it is the **momentum** of the ball that is important in the **collision** with the pins, and **momentum** depends on **mass** and **velocity**.

> **KEY POINT**
>
> **momentum** (kg m/s or N s) = **mass** (kg) × **velocity** (m/s)
> Momentum is a vector with the same direction as the velocity. The unit kg m/s is the same as the N s.

When a **force** acts on an object that is moving, or able to move, it causes a **change in momentum** in the same direction as the force (because the velocity changes). The longer **time** that the force acts, the bigger the change in momentum.

> **KEY POINT**
>
> **change in momentum** (kg m/s or N s) = **force** (N) × **time** (s)
> The time is the time for which the force acts:
> $$\text{force (N)} = \frac{\text{change in momentum (kg m/s or N s)}}{\text{time (s)}}$$

When two objects **collide** or **explode** apart, there is an equal and opposite force on each object, and they interact – push against each other – for the same time. This means that the **change in the momentum** of the objects is equal and opposite. Another way to say this is that the total momentum of the two objects before the collision or explosion is the same as the total momentum after the collision.

> **KEY POINT**
>
> If no external forces act on the colliding/exploding objects, the total momentum of objects before a collision/explosion is the same as the total momentum after the collision/explosion.
> This is called the **conservation of momentum**.

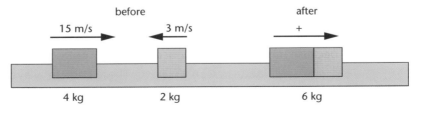

Fig. 9.13 Two objects colliding and sticking together.

Calculations using conservation of momentum are not required for Edexcel.

Taking the right direction to be positive:

Before the collision momentum =

$$4 \text{ kg} \times 15 \text{ m/s} + 2 \text{ kg} \times (-3)\text{m/s} = (60 - 6) \text{ kg m/s}$$

After the collision, momentum = 6 kg × v

So, because of conservation of momentum, v = 9 m/s

Safer collisions

OCR A	P4.3
OCR B	P3f
AQA	P2.13.4
EDEXCEL 360	P2.9

When your body is in a **collision**, a **force** brings it to a sudden stop. The larger the stopping force on the body, the more it is damaged. To reduce **damage** we must reduce the **force**. This means:

- reducing the acceleration (force = mass × acceleration) which means reducing the velocity of the body more slowly.

This the same as:

- reducing the momentum of the body more slowly.

  $$(\text{force} = \frac{\text{change of momentum}}{\text{time}})$$

If the collision takes place over a longer time, say 0.5 s instead of 0.05 s – ten times as long – then the stopping force will only be one tenth of the size. The time of a collision can be increased by using:

- **Crumple zones** The car occupants are in a strong safety cage. The front and back of the car are designed to crumple in a collision, increasing the distance and time over which the occupants are brought to a stop.

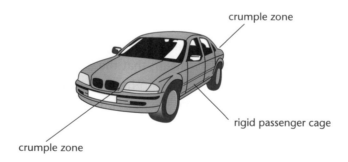

crumple zone

rigid passenger cage

crumple zone

Fig. 9.14 Crumple zones

- **Airbags** The body hits the airbag, which is compressed, increasing the distance the body moves and the time it takes to stop.
- **Seatbelts** These are designed to stretch slightly so that the body moves forward and comes to a stop more slowly than it would if it hit the windscreen or front seats. After a collision, the seatbelts should be replaced because having stretched once, they may not work properly again.
- **Cycle and motorcycle helmets** These contain a layer of material which will compress on impact so that the skull is brought to a stop more slowly. They should be replaced after a collision as the material will be damaged and may not give good protection again.

9.4 Work, energy and power

Work and energy

OCR A   P4.4
OCR B   P3d,e,h
AQA   P2.13.3
EDEXCEL 360   P2.10

For how to rearrange the formula see page 223.

Whenever a **force** makes something move, **work** is done. The amount of **work done** is equal to the amount of **energy transferred**. **Work**, like **energy**, is measured in **joules**.

> **KEY POINT**
> work done by a force (J) = force (N) × distance moved by force in direction of the force (m)

When work is done by something, it loses energy; when work is done on something it gains energy.

Gravitational potential energy

A rollercoaster at the top of a slope has **stored energy**, which is called **gravitational potential energy (GPE)**, or sometimes potential energy (PE). This is the name used to describe stored energy that an object has because of its position – in this case, higher above the surface of the Earth.

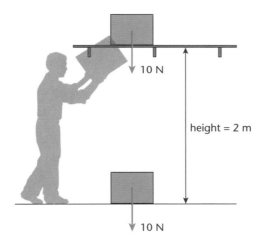

10 N

height = 2 m

10 N

Fig. 9.15 Doing work – increasing the GPE.

Fig. 9.15 shows that when you lift a 10 N weight (a mass of 1 kg) from the floor to a high shelf, a height difference of 2 m, you have done work on the weight. The work done = 10 N × 2 m = 20 J and this is equal to the increase in the GPE of the weight.

Edexcel uses *g* = acceleration of free fall. This is the same as the gravitational field strength *g* = 10 m/s² = 10 N/kg and the units are equivalent.

> **KEY POINT**
> Change in gravitational potential energy, GPE (J) = weight (N) × vertical height difference (m)
> or using *g* = the gravitational field strength (N/kg)
> change in GPE (J) = *m* (kg) × *g* (N/kg) × *h* (m)

On Earth, the gravitational field strength is $g = 10$ N/kg but on the Moon, because it is smaller g is only about one sixth of this. The size of g increases with the mass of the planet or star. In exams, you will always be given a value to use for g.

Kinetic energy (KE)

> **This explains why stopping distances increase by four times when the speed is doubled – there is four times the kinetic energy to transfer by the braking force.**

An object that is moving has **kinetic energy (KE)**. The energy depends on the **mass** of the object and on the **square** of the **speed** – doubling the speed gives four times the energy.

For example, an air hockey puck, floating on an air table, is almost frictionless. A **force** does **work** on the puck by pushing it a small **distance**. Energy is transferred increasing the **kinetic energy** of the puck – it speeds up. When the force stops the puck moves at a constant **speed** across the table – its **kinetic energy** is now constant.

> **For how to rearrange the formula see page 223.**

KEY POINT

A mass that is moving has kinetic energy:
kinetic energy (J) $= \frac{1}{2} \times$ mass (kg) $\times$ [speed (m/s)]^2
Or
kinetic energy (J) $= \frac{1}{2} \times$ mass (kg) $\times$ [velocity (m/s)]^2
Energy does not have a direction. Speed or velocity can be used to calculate the kinetic energy.

Roller coasters and falling

When frictional forces are small enough to be ignored, the transfer of energy between **KE** and **GPE** can be used to calculate **heights** and **speeds**. Fig. 9.16 shows a car that is driven by a trackside motor to the top of a rollercoaster slope and then freewheels down the slope.

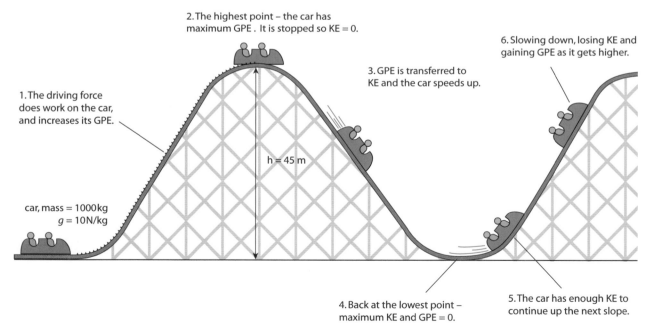

2. The highest point – the car has maximum GPE . It is stopped so KE = 0.

6. Slowing down, losing KE and gaining GPE as it gets higher.

3. GPE is transferred to KE and the car speeds up.

1. The driving force does work on the car, and increases its GPE.

h = 45 m

car, mass = 1000kg
g = 10N/kg

4. Back at the lowest point – maximum KE and GPE = 0.

5. The car has enough KE to continue up the next slope.

Fig. 9.16 Transferring energy from GPE to KE and back again.

Increase in GPE of train = $m\,g\,h$ = 1000 kg × 10 N/kg × 45 m = 450 000 J

Assuming there are no friction forces as the train travels down the slope:

loss of GPE = gain in KE

$$450\,000\,J = \tfrac{1}{2}\,m\,v^2 = \tfrac{1}{2} \times 1000\,kg \times v^2$$

$$v^2 = 900\,(m/s)^2 \text{ so speed} = 30\,m/s$$

Remember this equation.

Circular motion

EDEXCEL 360 **P2.10**

When a rollercoaster travels at a **constant speed** on a circular part of the track, it is **accelerating** – its velocity is changing because it is changing direction. There is a **resultant force** making the train move in a **circle**. The **resultant force** and the **acceleration** are directed **towards the centre** of the circle. This is always true for any object moving in a circular path.

In Fig. 9.17, a ball on a string moves in a circle. The **force** in this case is the **tension** in the string – cut the string and the ball flies off at a tangent – a straight line.

Fig. 9.17 A circular path needs a force towards the centre of the circle.

Work, friction and conservation of energy

OCR A **P4.4**
OCR B **P3h**
AQA **P2.13.3**
EDEXCEL 360 **P2.10**

You can only use the relationship '**gain in KE = loss in GPE**' for a falling object if the drag (air resistance) is small and can be ignored – or if the object is falling in a vacuum. The skydiver in Fig. 9.8 in 9.2 Resistance to motion – friction and drag, eventually reaches **terminal velocity**. He is still falling, so GPE is being lost, but no KE is being gained. The energy is being used to do **work against** the **frictional force** (drag) and the skydiver and surrounding air will **heat up**.

For an object like the space shuttle, with a lot of **KE**, heatproof tiles are needed to protect it from the **heat** resulting from doing **work against** the **drag** when it re-enters the Earth's atmosphere.

Another example is a cyclist travelling at a **steady speed**. Energy is being transferred by **heating** the bicycle and surroundings as **work** is done **against friction**. No energy is being transferred as KE to the bicycle unless it speeds up.

When **energy** is transferred to the surroundings by **heating** (for example due to frictional forces) it is no longer useful – but it is not lost. We say it has been **dissipated** (spread out) as **heat**. The **total energy** remains the same. This important result is called the **principle of conservation of energy**. Energy can be stored and transferred in different ways, but when it is all accounted for, the total amount stays the same.

> For AQA, you need to know that some objects can return to their original shape because elastic potential energy is stored in the object when work is done to change its shape.

Power

> OCR B — P3d
> EDEXCEL 360 — P2.10

Power is the **rate of energy transfer**. This is the **work done** or **energy transferred** divided by **time**.

> For how to rearrange the formula see page 223.

KEY POINT

$$\text{power (W)} = \frac{\text{work done or energy transferred (J)}}{\text{time (s)}}$$

power is measured in watts (W) when energy is in joules (J) and the time in seconds (s)

Fuel consumption

> OCR B — P3d,e

Fuel consumption is measured in **litres per km**. (We also uses miles per gallon as a measure of performance – a high figure is good.)

Larger vehicles, and those with a greater acceleration have **more powerful engines**, so that energy can be transferred more quickly from the fuel to do work. The **work done = driving force × distance travelled**. A more **powerful** engine can transfer more energy per second – this uses **more fuel**.

Energy from fuel is needed to:
- increase KE
- do work against friction.

When a car brakes, the KE is transferred to heat. Braking and accelerating repeatedly will transfer more energy than travelling at a constant speed. The amount of braking and accelerating will depend on **driving style** and the **road conditions** (e.g. single carriageway, lots of bends, traffic lights). At **higher speeds**, resistive forces are greater and more work is done against friction. If more energy is transferred the fuel consumption is increased (increasing cost, and pollution).

HOW SCIENCE WORKS

OCR A	P4.1
OCR B	P3a
AQA	2.13.1
EDEXCEL 360	P2.10

Relativity – how new scientific theories are introduced

Albert Einstein introduced a theory of motion known as the Theory of Relativity. The theory of motion you have studied in this chapter works for everyday speeds and situations. Einstein used his creative imagination to do a thought experiment – it was a new idea not based on any experimental data. For example, he suggested that nothing could travel faster than light – 300 million m/s.

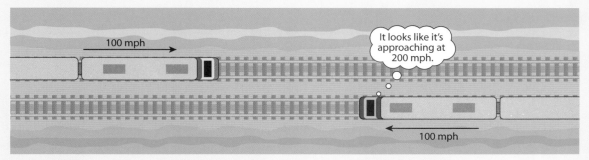

Fig. 9.18 From one train, the other appears to be approaching at 200 mph.

Imagine two trains approaching each other, both travelling at nine tenths (0.9) times the speed of light. If you are travelling on one of them and look at the other, it will appear to be rushing towards you at (0.9 + 0.9 = 1.8) times the speed of light. But, according to Einstein's theory, this is not possible – nothing can appear to travel faster than light. The explanation included mathematical proof that the mass of the trains increased as they got faster, and that time itself passed at a different rate depending on how fast you moved.

Another part of the Relativity Theory says that time passes at a different rate depending on the gravitational field strength. Some scientists were very reluctant to accept the new theories, as, at first, there was no evidence to show these effects. In 1919 the distortion of starlight during an eclipse provided evidence that convinced many scientists.

They also predicted other effects that could be measured to see if the theory was correct. By 1971, an accurate and stable atomic clock was available to test the theory by flying four atomic clocks around the world for three days. When they returned, and the clocks were compared, they confirmed Einstein's Relativity Theory.

This table shows the average of the time differences measured on all the clocks. All the results were within a range of ±23 nm from the average value. The time differences are very small (1 ns = 0.000000001 s = 1×10^{-9} s.)

	Average time shift (ns)	
	Travelling East	**Travelling west**
predicted	– 40	+ 275
measured	– 59	+ 273

HOW SCIENCE WORKS

In normal everyday life, you do not notice the effects, but if you use a SatNav system or a GPS receiver they take relativity into account when they work out your position. They need to do this because the signal travels very fast to satellites and back.

HOW SCIENCE WORKS *Questions*

1. From the passage above, write down of an example of something that Einstein said changed, but previous theories said was constant. **[1]**

2. Other scientists were reluctant to accept Einstein's ideas because:

    A they didn't want to change the theory of motion they were using

    B he didn't have any evidence – it was a mathematical theory

    C they each wanted to find a new theory.

    D his evidence didn't match his predictions **[1]**

3. Some scientists said they would not have been convinced if the time measurements had a range of ± 300 nm from the average value. Why not? **[2]**

4. It was over 60 years after Einstein's proposal before these measurements were made to prove the theory. Why was there such a long delay? **[1]**

Exam practice questions

1. This graph shows the movement of a car:

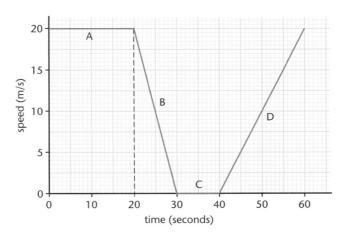

   (a) In which section, **A B C** or **D** is the car:

   (i) accelerating (speeding up) ?

   (ii) stopped? [2]

   (b) How far does the car travel in the first 20 seconds?

   A 0 m **B** 20 m **C** 40 m **D** 400 m [1]

   (c) The **instantaneous speed** of the car after 50 seconds is:

   A 0 m/s **B** 1 m/s **C** 10 m/s **D** 20 m/s [1]

2. Choose words from this list to complete the sentences below. A word may be used once, more than once or not at all.

action	backward	drive	equal	foot	force	forward
friction	ground	opposite	pair	reaction		

   Walking involves a ____1____ of forces. The forces are ____2____ and ____3____ and are known as the ____4____ and ____5____ force. The ____6____ pushes ____7____ on the ____8____ and the ____9____ pushes ____10____ on the ____11____ . If there is no ____12____ you cannot walk. [4]

3. These statements describe what happens during a parachute jump.

A	The parachute opens – increasing the drag force
B	His speed increases and the drag force increases
C	The drag force becomes equal to his weight
D	The skydiver steps from the aircraft and falls, he accelerates at 10 m/s^2
E	He falls with a constant speed
F	His speed decreases

   Put them in the correct order. The first has been done for you.

D					

   [4]

Exam practice questions

4. Use the equation: momentum = mass × velocity
to match the values of momentum to the situations. The car is travelling in the positive direction:

Situation

A	A car of mass 1000 kg and velocity +28 m/s
B	A lorry of mass 2800 kg and velocity −10 m/s travelling towards a car of mass 1000 kg and velocity +28 m/s
C	A car of mass 1400 kg that is travelling at −10 m/s towards a lorry of mass 2800 kg and velocity + 10 m/s
D	A lorry of mass 2800 kg and velocity +10 m/s travelling towards a car of mass 1000 kg and velocity +10 m/s

Total momentum

1	0 kg m/s
2	28000 kg m/s
3	38000 kg m/s
4	14000 kg m/s

[3]

5. This diagram shows a roller coaster track.

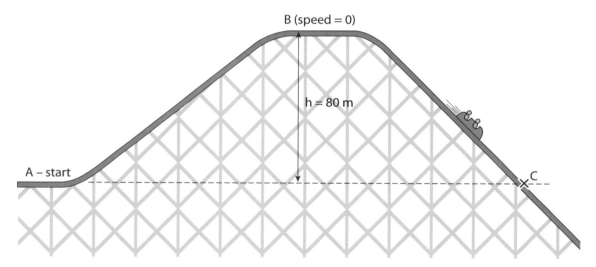

The mass of a car is 800 kg
Gravitational field strength = 10 N/kg

Change in PE = mass × gravitational field strength × height difference
KE = $\frac{1}{2}$ mass × velocity^2
Work done = force × distance

Assume there are no energy losses due to friction as the car goes round the track.

(a) What is the increase in potential energy when the car moves from A to B?

(b) What is the kinetic energy at point C?

(c) What is the speed of the car at point C?

(d) At the end of the ride, the kinetic energy of the car is 25 000 J and it brakes to a stop in 10 m. What is the braking force? **[4]**

Exam practice questions

6. A van with mass 3000 kg travels at a steady speed of 30 m/s.
The resistive force is 5000 N.

    (a) What is the driving force on the van in newtons? **[1]**

    (b) Using KE = $\frac{1}{2}$ mass × velocity² work out the kinetic energy of the van. **[1]**

    (c) and **(d)** depend on the specification. Choose either for Edexcel and AQA.

The van stops in 5 seconds.

OCR A **(c)** Using momentum = mass × velocity work out the momentum of the van.

    (d) Using force = $\frac{\text{change in momentum}}{\text{time}}$ work out the force stopping the van.

    or

OCR B **(c)** Using acceleration = $\frac{\text{change in velocity}}{\text{time}}$ work out the acceleration of the van.

    (d) using force = mass × acceleration work out the force stopping the van. **[2]**

7. This table shows the shortest stopping distances for a car at different speeds.

Speed mph	Thinking distance (m)	Braking distance (m)	Stopping distance (m)
20	6	6	12
40	12	24	?
60	18	55	73

    (a) Work out the missing value for the stopping distance at 40 mph. **[1]**

    (b) These are the shortest stopping distances. Describe a factor that will increase:
        (i) the thinking distance
        (ii) the braking distance. **[2]**

    (c) In a collision test, a dummy with mass 60 kg is travelling at 20 m/s. Work out the kinetic energy of the dummy.
        (KE = $\frac{1}{2}$ mass × velocity²) **[1]**

When the dummy hits the windscreen it stops in 0.001 s
When the dummy is wearing a seatbelt it stops in 0.02 s

    (d) What happens to the seatbelt to make the stopping time longer? **[1]**
    (e) How does this reduce the damage to the dummy? **[1]**

Studies show that when some drivers wear seat belts, they drive faster and the injuries and deaths of pedestrians increase.

    (f) Explain why a driver might increase speed when wearing a seatbelt. **[2]**

Hannah travels every day by car. She does not want to travel by train because she thinks it may crash. This chart gives information about deaths on the roads and railways in the UK in 2004.

UK 2005	Roads	Railways
Deaths	1675	5
Death rate	3.3 travellers per billion vehicle kilometres	0.1 travellers per billion passenger kilometres

    (g) In the table, which has higher risk, road or rail travel? **[1]**
    (h) Suggest a reason why Hannah thinks that rail travel is more dangerous than road travel. **[2]**

Chapter

10 Electricity

The following topics are covered in this chapter:

- *Electrostatics*
- *Electric circuits*
- *The mains electricity supply*

10.1 Electrostatics

Electric charge

OCR A — P5.1
OCR B — P4a
AQA — P2.13.5
EDEXCEL 360 — P2.12

Electric charge can be **positive** or **negative**. **Electrons** are particles with a negative electric charge. They can move freely through a **conductor**, for example, any type of **metal**, but no charged particles can move through an **insulator**.

Materials that are positively charged have missing electrons, materials that are negatively charged have extra electrons

Electrostatic effects are caused by the transfer of **electrons**. (This is sometimes called **static electricity**.) When **insulators** are rubbed, **electrons** are rubbed off one material and **transferred** to the other.

Fig. 10.1 shows a polythene rod rubbed with a duster. It has picked up **electrons** from the duster and becomes negatively charged leaving the duster positively charged.

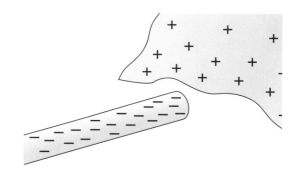

Fig. 10.1 The insulated rod and the cloth have opposite charge.

Conductors cannot be charged unless they are completely surrounded by **insulating materials**, like dry air and plastic – otherwise the electrons flow to or from the conductor to discharge it. An **insulated conductor** can be charged by rubbing with a **charged duster**, or touching it with a **charged rod**. Some electrons will be transferred, so that the charge is spread out over both objects.

> **KEY POINT**
> Two objects **attract** each other if one is **positively charged** and the other is **negatively charged**. Two objects with **similar charge** (both **positive** or both **negative**) **repel**.

Remember: Like charges **repel** and unlike charges **attract**.

A conductor can be **discharged** by touching it with another conductor, such as a wire, so that electrons flow along the wire and cancel out the charge.

The earth connection

To stop conductors becoming charged, we sometimes use a thick metal wire to connect them to a large metal plate in the ground. This acts as a large reservoir of electrons. We say the object is connected to **earth**, or **earthed**.

Electrons flow so quickly to or from earth that earthed objects do not become charged. If all the metal water pipes in a house are connected into the ground like this, they can be used as an earth.

Dangers of electrostatic charge

The **human body** conducts electricity. When the flow of charge is large enough for our **nerves** and **muscles** to be affected, we call this an **electric shock**. **Electrostatic shocks** are usually small and not harmful. For example those from touching a car door on a dry day when charge has built up on the metal car and flows through you to earth. Larger ones can be dangerous to people with heart problems because a flow of charge through the body can **stop** the **heart**. **Lightning** is a very large **electrostatic discharge**. When it flows through a body it is often fatal.

If you are standing on an **insulating mat** or wearing shoes with **insulating soles** when you touch a charged object, then this will reduce the chance of an electric shock because the charge will not flow through you to earth. You will become charged, and stay charged until you touch a conductor.

Explosions

When a charged object is close to a conductor, electrons can jump across the gap. This is a spark and can cause an explosion if there are:

inflammable vapours like petrol or methanol

powders in the air, like flour or custard, which contain lots of oxygen – as a dust they can explode

inflammable gases like hydrogen or methane

Fig. 10.2 sparks can cause explosions.

Lorries containing inflammable gases, liquids and powders are connected to earth before loading or unloading. Aircraft are earthed before being refuelled. This prevents charge from building up on metal pipes or tanks when the loads are moved, so there is no danger of a spark igniting the load.

Annoying electrostatic charge

Charged objects attract small particles of dust and dirt, for example, plastic cases and TV monitors.

Clothing can be charged as you move and 'clings' to other items of clothing, or the body. Synthetic fibres are affected more than natural fibres as they are better insulators.

Anti-static sprays, liquids and cloths stop the build up of static charge. These work by increasing the amount of conduction – sometimes by attracting moisture because water conducts electricity.

Uses – photocopiers and laser printers

In a **photocopier**:
- a rubber belt is coated with a material that conducts electricity only when it is illuminated
- the belt is charged
- a bright light is used to make an image of the sheet of paper to be copied on the belt

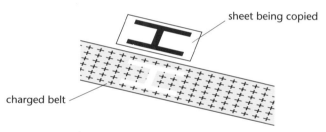

Fig. 10.3 Making a photocopy.

- the illuminated parts of the belt discharge
- the belt is sprayed with black powder that sticks to the charged areas
- a sheet of paper is pressed on the belt so the black powder is transferred
- the paper is heated to make the powder stick to the sheet.

A **laser printer** is very similar, but instead of a bright light making an image of the page, a laser light beam is used to write the characters on the belt.

Uses – Electrostatic precipitators

Electrostatic precipitators remove dust or smoke particles from chimneys, so that they are not carried out of the chimney by the hot air.
- Metal plates or grids are put in the chimneys.
- They are charged by connecting them to a high voltage.
- The smoke particles are attracted to the charged plates or grids.
- The particles clump together on the plates to form larger particles.
- When they are heavy enough, the smoke particles fall back down the chimney into containers.

The grids are positively charged in some designs and negatively charged in others.

Uses – Paint spraying

OCR B   P4b

The **paint** and the object are given different charges so that the paint is **attracted** to the object.

- The spray gun is charged so that it charges the paint particles.
- The paint particles repel each other to give a fine spray.
- The object is charged with the opposite charge to the paint.
- The object attracts the paint.
- The paint makes an even coat, it even gets underneath and into parts that are in shadow.
- Less paint is wasted.

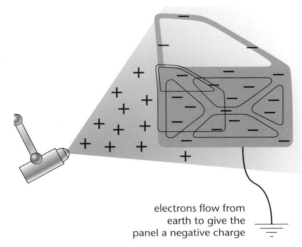

electrons flow from earth to give the panel a negative charge

Fig. 10.4 Paint spraying.

Uses – Defibrillators

OCR B   P4b

When the heart beats, it is the heart muscle contracting. A **defibrillator** is used to start the heart when it has stopped beating regularly.

- Two electrodes called paddles are placed on the patient's chest.
- Everyone, including the operator must 'stand clear' so they don't get an electric shock.
- The paddles are charged.
- The charge is passed from one paddle, through the chest to the other paddle to make the heart muscle contract.

> The paddles must make a good electrical contact with the patient's chest.

Uses – Fingerprinting

EDEXCEL 360 P2.12

If a dust print is left on a surface this can be lifted using charged **lifting film**.

- The lifting film is made of material that stores electrostatic charge.
- The film is placed over the print.
- The dust particles are attracted and stick to the film.
- The print is stored on the film.

10.2 Electric circuits

Circuit symbols

OCR A — P5.2,3,4
OCR B — P4c
AQA — P2.13.6

More than one cell used to be called a 'battery of cells'. Now 'battery' is often used to mean one cell. OCR A refers to one battery, but other specifications expect you to use the word 'cell'.

For OCR A you need to know that current is a flow of positive charge so the direction of the current is opposite to the direction of the electron flow, because electrons are negatively charged.

Component	Symbol	Component	Symbol
switch (open)		lamp	
switch (closed)		fuse	
cell		fixed resistor	
battery		variable resistor	
ammeter		light dependent resistor (LDR)	
voltmeter		thermistor	
junction of conductors		diode	
motor		generator	
power supply		a.c. power supply	

Electric current and charge

OCR A — P5.1
OCR B — P4c
AQA — P2.13.5,8

Electric current:

- is a flow of electric **charge**
- only flows if there is a **compete circuit**. Any break in the circuit switches it off
- is measured in **amperes** (A) using an **ammeter**
- is not used up in a circuit. If there is only one route around a circuit, the current will be the **same** wherever it is measured
- transfers energy to the components in the circuit.

Some people prefer not to say 'current flows' because this means 'a flow of charge flows.' Others find it helps them to picture what is happening.

KEY POINT An electric current is a flow of electric charge.

Series circuits

OCR A   P5.3
OCR B   P4c
AQA   P2.13.6

A **series** circuit is a circuit with only one route around it. Fig. 10.5 shows a lamp and motor connected in series to a battery with two ammeters in series to measure the current through the lamps. The current measured on each ammeter will be the same.

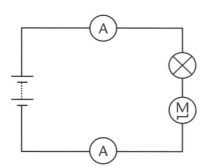

Fig. 10.5 A series circuit.

Parallel circuits

OCR A   P5.3
AQA   P2.12.6

A **parallel** circuit has more than one path for the current around the circuit. Fig. 10.6 shows a motor and a lamp connected in parallel to a battery. There are two paths (marked in red and blue) around the circuit so the current measured on ammeters B and C adds up to give current measured on ammeter A and on ammeter D.

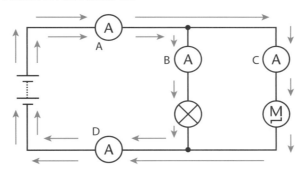

Fig. 10.6 A parallel circuit.

Voltage (also called potential difference)

OCR A   P5.3
AQA   P2.13.5,6

Voltage is also called **potential difference (p.d)**. It is:
- measured between two points in a circuit
- measured in **volts** (V) using a **voltmeter**
- a measure of **energy transferred** to (or from) the charge moving between the two points
- measured between the terminals of a battery, or other power supply, when the energy is transferred to the charge
- measured between the ends of a component when the energy is transferred from the charge.

> The higher the voltage of a battery, the higher the 'push' on the charges in the circuit.

When components are connected in **series**, as shown in Fig. 10.7, the voltage, or potential difference (p.d.) of the power supply is shared between the components.

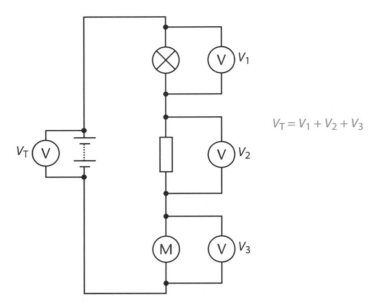

$$V_T = V_1 + V_2 + V_3$$

Fig. 10.7 Adding the measurements on the three voltmeters gives the power supply p.d.

> **Remember, it is 'current through' but 'voltage across' a component.**

When components are connected in parallel to a power supply, as shown in Fig. 10.8, the voltage, or potential difference (p.d), across each component is the same as that of the power supply.

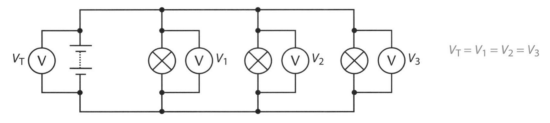

$$V_T = V_1 = V_2 = V_3$$

Fig 10.8 The measurements on all the voltmeters are the same.

> **Ammeters are connected in series. Voltmeters are connected in parallel.**

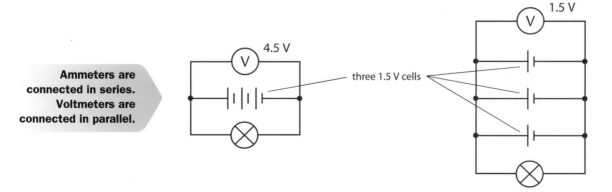

Fig. 10.9 Cells connected in series and in parallel.

Resistance and resistors

OCR A | **P5.2**
OCR B | **P4c**
AQA | **P2.13.6**

All the components and wires in a circuit **resist** the flow of electric charge through them.

When the **voltage** is fixed (for example, by using a battery) the larger the **resistance** of a circuit, the less **current** passes through it.

The resistance of the connecting wires is so small it can usually be ignored. Other metals have a larger resistance, for example the filament of a light bulb is very large. **Metals** get **hot** when charge flows through them. The larger the resistance, the hotter they get. A light bulb filament gets so hot that it glows.

KEY POINT

$$resistance = \frac{voltage}{current}$$

Resistance is measured in ohms (Ω) where current is in amperes (A) and voltage in volts (V)

$R = \dfrac{V}{I}$ and also $V = IR$ and $I = \dfrac{V}{R}$

For how to rearrange the formula see page 223.

Fixed resistors

OCR A | **P5.2**
AQA | **P2.13.6**

In some components, such as **resistors** and **metal conductors**, the resistance stays constant when the current and voltage change, providing that the temperature does not change.

For this type of fixed resistance if the **voltage** is increased (for example, by adding another battery), the **current** increases. A graph of current against voltage is a straight line, because the **current** is **directly proportional** to the **voltage** – doubling the voltage doubles the current. Components that obey this law (sometimes called Ohm's Law) are sometimes called **ohmic** components or devices.

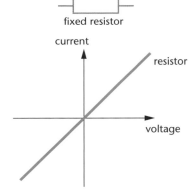

Fig. 10.10 A graph of current against voltage for a resistor.

Changing resistance

OCR A | **P5.2**
OCR B | **P4c**
AQA | **P2.13.6**

Variable resistors

A **variable resistor** changes the current in a circuit by changing the resistance. This can be used to change how circuits work, for example, to change:
- how long the shutter is open on a digital camera
- the loudness of the sound from a radio loud speaker
- the brightness of a bulb
- the speed of a motor.

Inside one type of variable resistor is a long piece of wire made of metal with a large resistance (called **resistance wire**). To alter the resistance of the circuit a sliding contact is moved along the wire to alter the length of wire in the circuit, as shown in Fig. 10.11.

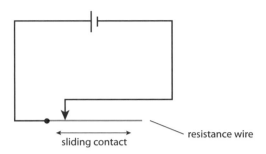

Fig. 10.11 A variable resistor design.

Filament lamps

The wire in a **filament lamp** gets hotter for larger currents. This increases the resistance so the graph of current against voltage is not a straight line.

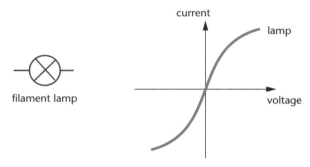

Fig. 10.12 A graph of current against voltage for a filament lamp.

Light dependent resistor (LDRs)

The resistance of a **light dependent resistor (LDR)** decreases as the light falling on it increases. This can be used in a circuit to control when a lamp switches on or off.

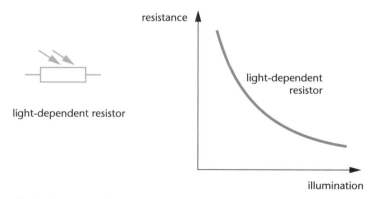

Fig. 10.13 A graph of resistance against intensity of light for a light-dependent resistor.

Thermistors

OCR A   P5.2
AQA   P2.13.6

The resistance of a negative temperature coefficient (NTC) **thermistor** decreases as the temperature increases. This can be used to switch on a heating or cooling circuit at a certain temperature.

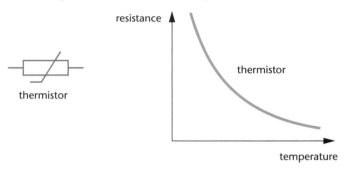

Fig. 10.14 A graph of resistance against temperature for a thermistor.

Diode

AQA   P2.13.6

Current will only flow through a **diode** in one direction. In one direction its resistance is very low, but in the other direction, called the **reverse direction**, its resistance is very high.

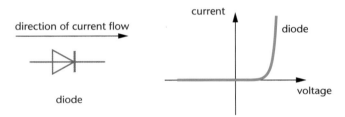

Fig. 10.15 A graph of current against voltage for a diode.

Combining resistors

OCR A   P5.2,3
AQA   P2.13.6

Components can be added to a circuit in series or in parallel, as shown in Fig. 10.16.

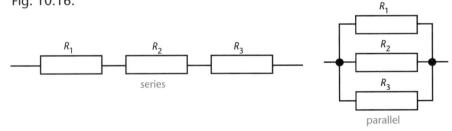

Fig. 10.16 Resistors connected in series and in parallel.

For components in **series**:
- Two (or more) components in **series** have more resistance than one on its own because the battery has to push charges through both of them.
- The **current** is the **same** through each component.
- The **p.d.** is **largest** across the component with the **largest resistance** because more energy is transferred by the charge passing through a large resistance than through a small one.

- The **p.d.s** across the components **add** up to give the p.d. of the **power supply**.

KEY POINT

When components are connected in series, the total resistance of the circuit is equal to sum of the resistances of all the components.

$R_T = R_1 + R_2 + R_3$

Where R_T is the total resistance of components with resistances R_1, R_2 and R_3 connected in series.

For components in **parallel**:

- A combination of two (or more) components in **parallel** has less resistance than one component on its own. This is because there is more than one path for charges to flow through.
- The **current** through each component is the same as if it were the only component present.
- The **total current** will be **sum** of the currents through all the components.
- The **p.d.** across all the components will be the **same** as the power supply **p.d.**
- The **current** is **largest** through the component with the **smallest resistance**. This is because the same battery voltage makes a larger current flow through a small resistance than through a large one.

A theory of resistance

OCR A   **P5.2**

Metals are made of a fixed **lattice** of atom centres surrounded by **free electrons**. The moving electrons form the current. In metals with low resistance, the electrons require less of a 'push' (p.d) to get through the lattice. The moving electrons **collide** with the stationary atom centres and make them **vibrate more**. This is a heating effect and increases the temperature of the metal.

10.3   *The mains electricity supply*

Safe use of mains electricity

OCR B   **P4c**
AQA   **P2.13.7**

The table shows the colour code for the mains electricity cables used in buildings, and in appliances.

Name of wire	Colour of insulation	Function of the wire
live	brown	carries the high voltage
neutral	blue	the second wire to complete the circuit
earth	green and yellow	a safety wire to stop the appliance becoming live

Fig. 10.16 shows how the plug is wired for a heater with a metal case. The **fuse** is always connected to the brown, **live** wire. A **cable grip** is tightened where the cable enters the plug to stop the wires being pulled out.

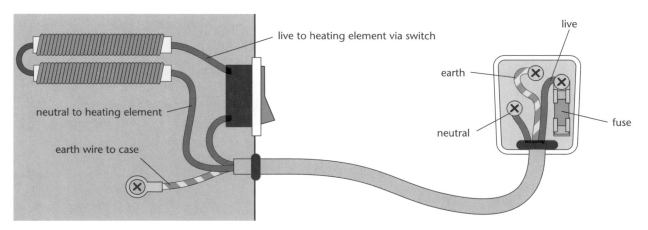

Fig. 10.17 A 3-pin plug on an earthed metal appliance.

KEY POINT

A **fuse** is a piece of wire that is thinner than the other wires in the circuit and will melt first if too much current flows and the wires overheat. A 3A fuse will melt if a current of 3A flows through it. The value of the fuse should be the lowest value that is more than the normal operating current.

For AQA you need to decide the correct fuse. Calculate the current and choose the lowest fuse that is higher than this value.

If there is a fault, or if too many appliances are plugged into one socket, resulting in a large current, then the fuse will melt and break the circuit preventing a fire.

The **earth** wire is connected to the metal case of metal appliances so that when they are plugged into the mains supply, the metal case is earthed (see 10.1 The earth connection) If there is a fault and the live wire touches the metal case, a very large current flows through the low-resistance path to earth melting the fuse wire and breaking the circuit.

Double insulated appliances have cases that do not conduct (usually plastic) and no metal parts you can touch so they do not need an earth wire.

The **fuse** takes a short time to melt, so it will not prevent you from getting an electric shock, which can be fatal, if you touch a live appliance.

Appliances that are particularly dangerous are those like lawn mowers and power tools, where the cable could get wet, or be cut. Music amplifiers are also dangerous where you are touching the metal instrument and there may be a lot of electrical equipment around that has not been safety tested. These should be connected using an **RCD (residual current device)** also called a **RCCB (residual current circuit breaker)**. These are switches to cut off the electricity very quickly if they detect a difference in the current flowing in the live and the neutral wires. (This would happen, for example, if the current was flowing through a person, or appliance casing.) Another advantage is that they can be switched back on once the fault is fixed, whereas a fuse must be replaced. An **RCD** can be part of mains circuit in a building, or a plug-in device that goes between the appliance and the socket.

Electrical energy and power

For OCR A, you need to revise efficiency, which you learned about in P3.3, so you can calculate efficiency of electrical appliances.

Sound is made by the movement of a loudspeaker cone.

We use electrical appliances at home to transfer energy from the mains supply to:

* heating
* light
* movement (including sound).

In two hours, an electric lamp transforms twice as much energy as it transforms in one hour. The **power** of an electrical appliance indicates how much **electrical energy** it transfers in one **second** – in other words, the rate at which it transfers electrical energy into other forms of energy.

> **KEY POINT**
>
> Power is measured in watts (W) where 1 W = 1 J/s.

Appliances used for heating have a much higher power rating than those used to produce light or sound.

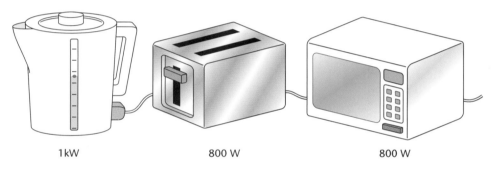

1kW   800 W   800 W

Fig. 10.18 Power ratings of electrical appliances.

The amount of **energy transferred** from the mains appliance depends on the **power** rating of the appliance and the **time** for which it is switched on. Energy is measured in joules, but electricity suppliers sell us electrical energy in **units** called **kilowatt-hours**. Electricity meters measure the energy transferred in kilowatt-hours.

The kilowatt-hour is a unit of energy – not power. (Power is measured in watts or kilowatts.)

> **KEY POINT**
>
> Electrical energy is calculated by:
> Energy = power × time
>   **E = Pt**
> There are two sets of units used for energy:
> * **The energy is in joules (J) when the power is in watts and the time is in seconds.**
> * **The energy is in kilowatt-hours (kW h) when the power is in kilowatts and the time is in hours.**

The cost of each unit of electrical energy – which is one kilowatt-hour of electrical energy – varies. At the moment it is about 10p. The electrical energy bill is calculated by working out the number of units used and multiplying by the cost of a unit.

For how to rearrange the formula see page 223.

KEY POINT

Cost of electrical energy used is calculated from:
Cost = power in kW × time in hours × cost of one unit
or
Cost = number of kW h used × cost of one unit

For example:
For the 800 W microwave oven in Fig.10.18:
if it is used for half an hour and the cost of a unit is 10p:
$$\text{Cost} = 0.8\,\text{kW} \times 0.5\,\text{hours} \times 10\text{p/kW h}$$
$$\text{Cost} = 0.4\text{p}$$

Power current and voltage

 OCR A **P5.5**
AQA **P2.13.8**

For how to rearrange the formula see page 223.

KEY POINT

Electrical power is worked out using:
Power = current × voltage
P = IV
Power is measured in watts (W), current in amperes (A) and voltage in volts (V).

Energy and charge

 AQA **P2.13.8**

KEY POINT

Electric charge is measured in coulombs (C)
charge (C) = current (A) x time(s)

KEY POINT

The energy transformed in a circuit depends on the charge that has flowed and the potential difference.
energy transformed (J) = potential difference (V) x charge (C)

How generators work

OCR A **P5.4**

The diagram shows how a voltage is **induced** in a coil of wire by **moving** a **magnet** into or out of a **coil**. Moving the coil instead of the magnet would have the same effect. This effect is used in **dynamos** and **generators**.

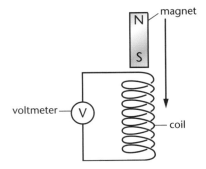

Fig. 10.19 A voltage is induced.

KEY POINT

The **dynamo effect** occurs when a voltage is induced by:
- moving a magnet near a coil
- moving a coil near a magnet.

There are three ways to increase the induced **voltage** (and get greater induced **current**):

- use stronger magnets
- use more turns of wire in the coil
- move the magnet (or the coil) faster.

The diagram shows a bicycle dynamo that uses a rotating magnet. As the magnet rotates

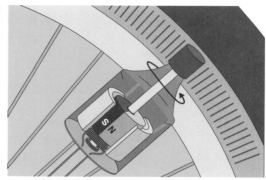

Fig. 10.20 A bicycle dynamo.

faster, the induced current increases and the bicycle light gets brighter.

A generator in a power station uses an **electromagnet** to produce a **magnetic field**. The electromagnet rotates inside **coils of wire** so that the coil is in a **changing magnetic field** and a voltage is induced.

Alternating current (a.c.) and direct current (d.c.)

OCR A **P5.4**
AQA **P2.13.7**

Changing the direction of the **magnetic field** or the **movement** induces a voltage in the opposite direction. As the magnet rotates, the north pole and south pole swap over once in each complete rotation. This means the direction of the voltage and the current changes. This is called **alternating current (a.c.)**.

> **KEY POINT**
> Dynamos and a.c. generators produce alternating current (a.c.). Batteries and solar cells produce direct current (d.c.).

> The size of d.c. can change but it is always in the same direction. For a.c. a graph of the voltage alternates in the same way as a graph of the current.

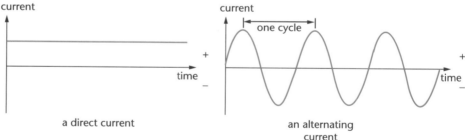

Fig. 10.21 d.c. and a.c.

> For AQA to work out the period from an oscilloscope display:
> • measure one cycle on the screen
> • multiply by the timebase scale.
> Frequency = 1 ÷ period

In the UK, the a.c. generators at power stations that supply our mains electricity rotate **50 times in one second**. This means that there are 50 complete cycles each second. The number of cycles per second is called the **frequency**. Frequency is measured in cycles per second or in hertz (Hz), where 1 Hz = 1 cycle per second.

> **KEY POINT**
> in the UK, the mains frequency is 50 Hz, which is 50 cycles per second.

More about electromagnetic induction

OCR A   P5.4

Electromagnetic induction is the name of the process where a changing magnetic field induces a voltage in a conductor. It is used in generators and in transformers. If there is an **induced voltage** in a coil and the ends are connected to make a complete circuit then a current flows in the coil.

Fig. 10.22 shows how the current in the coil of a generator changes with the rotation of the magnet or electromagnet.

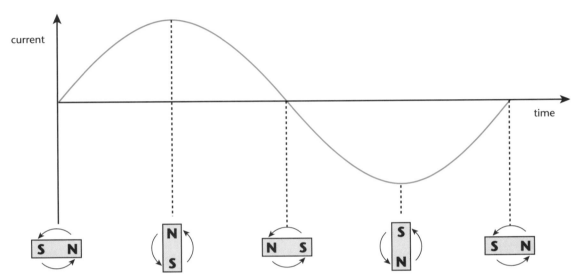

Fig. 10.22 How a rotating magnet changes the current in the coil.

In a generator, the induced voltage can be increased by:
- increasing the speed of rotation of the magnet or electromagnet
- increasing the strength of the magnetic field
- increasing the number of turns on the coil
- placing an iron core in the coil.

The a.c. mains supply voltage is 230 V. We use a.c. for the mains supply because it is easier to generate than d.c. and can be distributed more efficiently.

Transformers

OCR A   P5.4

A changing magnetic field is needed so transformers will not work with a d.c. supply.

A **transformer** changes the size of an **alternating voltage**. One of the reasons we use an a.c. mains supply is so that we can change voltage using transformers.

Step-up transformers increase voltage, and **step-down** transformers decrease voltage.

Fig. 10.23 shows how a transformer is made. There are two coils, **a primary coil** and **a secondary coil**. The iron core concentrates the magnetic field in the coils.
- An alternating current in the primary coil produces a changing magnetic field.
- The changing magnetic field induces a voltage in the secondary coil..

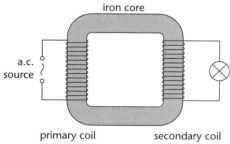

iron core

a.c. source

primary coil   secondary coil

Fig. 10.23 A transformer.

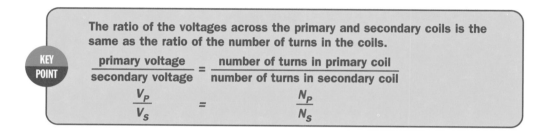

KEY POINT

The ratio of the voltages across the primary and secondary coils is the same as the ratio of the number of turns in the coils.

$$\frac{\text{primary voltage}}{\text{secondary voltage}} = \frac{\text{number of turns in primary coil}}{\text{number of turns in secondary coil}}$$

$$\frac{V_P}{V_S} = \frac{N_P}{N_S}$$

The National Grid

The National Grid is the network of suppliers of electricity – the power stations and users of electricity – homes and workplaces. They are all connected together by power lines, some overhead and some underground.

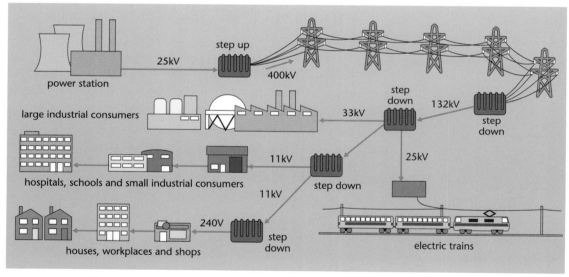

Fig. 10.24 The National Grid.

A National Grid has the following advantages:
- Power stations can be built where the fuel reserves are, or near the sea or rivers for cooling.
- Pollution can be kept away from cities.
- Power can be diverted to where it is needed, if there is high demand or a breakdown.
- Surplus power can be used to pump water up into reservoirs to be used to generate hydroelectric power when there is a peak in demand. (Dinorwig in Wales is a pumped storage power station.)
- Very large power stations can be built which are more efficient.

A National Grid has the following disadvantages:
● Power is wasted heating the power cables.
● Overhead power cables are an eyesore.
● Smaller generating projects such as wind turbines and panels of solar cells have difficulty competing with large suppliers.

Reducing power loss in power lines

To supply 100 kW of power through overhead power lines we could transmit 1 A at 100 V or 10 A at 10 V. (Using $P = IV$ the power is $P = 1 \text{ A} \times 100 \text{ V} = 100$ kW or $P = 10 \text{ A} \ 10 \text{ V} = 100 \text{ kW}$)

The power lines have a resistance to the flow of current. The heating effect in the cables depends on the resistance and on the current in the cables. By making the current as small as possible we can reduce the energy wasted as heat in the cables. The current can be small if the voltage is large.

We reduce the resistance of the cable by using thick copper, but the advantage of lower resistance has to be balanced against increased cost of cables and supports for the heavier cables.

KEY POINT

When supplying power through cables, a large voltage allows us to use a small current and this reduces energy waste by reducing the heating of the cables.

Transformers are used to **step-up** the voltage. Several different voltages are used, for example the supergrid is at 400 kV. **Step-down** transformers reduce this for us to use, for example to 230 V in our homes.

HOW SCIENCE WORKS

Jack and Emily set up a circuit to measure the current through a resistor for different values of the voltage across the resistor. Between each measurement, they switch off the circuit to make sure that it doesn't heat up. Fig. 10.25 shows the circuit they used, their results and a graph they plotted.

Voltage (volts)	Current (milliamps)			
	1st reading	2nd reading	3rd reading	Average reading
0	0	0	0	0
0.5	2.0	2.6	2.0	2.2
1.0	5.0	5.2	4.8	5.0
1.5	7.5	7.4	7.6	7.5
2.0	10.3	8.8	9.9	10.1
2.5	11.8	12.4	13.0	12.4
3.0	14.8	15.0	15.5	15.1

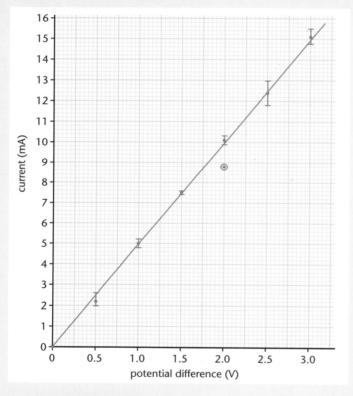

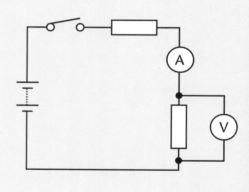

Fig. 10.25

In this experiment:
- voltage is the **independent variable** (the variable that Jack and Emily changed), so it is plotted on the horizontal axis
- current is the **dependent variable** (it changes when the voltage changes), so it is plotted on the vertical axis
- temperature is a **control variable** (it will affect the results if it changes, so Jack and Emily take care to keep it constant)
- all of these **variables** are **continuous** (or **contiguous**), they can take any value on a sliding scale. A **discrete variable** is one that has only set values, for example the number of components in the circuit, or the number of measurements taken.

HOW SCIENCE WORKS

To calculate an **average** measurement for the current, Jack adds the three measurements together and divides by three, because there are three measurements.

He says that one of the values for the current is obviously wrong, so he is not including it. A result like this is called an **outlier** or an **anomalous result**. He calculates an average of the other two measurements.

Emily plots error bars on the points to show the **range** of the measurements. The smaller the range, the more **reliable** the average measurement. She draws a **best straight line** through the points. This is one straight line, not a lot of separate straight sections.

1. Which of these variables is discrete?
   A   number of batteries
   B   voltage
   C   current
   D   electrical resistance   [1]
2. Which of the measurements for current and p.d. has Jack decided is an outlier?   [1]
3. What is the p.d. for the current measurement that has the greatest range? [1]
4. Emily takes one more measurement at 3.5 V. The current measurements are 17.3 mA, 17.9 mA and 18.2 mA. Work out **(a)** the range and **(b)** average current value.   [2]

Exam practice questions

1.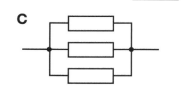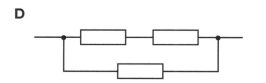

   All the resistors in these combinations are identical. Which of the combinations has the largest resistance? [1]

2. The energy wasted in electrical cables can be reduced by transmitting energy through cables with:
   A a high current
   B a high heat capacity
   C a high resistance
   D a high voltage [1]

3. What size fuse should be fitted to a plug for a 500 W hairdryer?
   (mains supply voltage = 230 V)
   A 1 A
   B 3 A
   C 5 A
   D 13 A [1]

4. Draw straight lines to link the **electrical component** to the correct **symbol**

Electrical component	**Symbol**
light dependent resistor (LDR)	
thermistor	
fuse	

   [3]

5. Put these steps in order to describe how a transformer works.
   A The induced voltage makes an alternating current flow in the coil.
   B The alternating voltage across the primary coil produces a changing magnetic field.
   C The changing magnetic field induces an alternating voltage in the secondary coil.
   D The magnetic field changes in the secondary coil.
   E The magnetic field changes in the iron core. [4]

Exam practice questions

6. Choose words from the list to complete this description of how a defibrillator can restart the heart. (Use words once, more than once or not at all.)

charge   **chest**   **contract**   **electrical**   **head**   **shock**   **stop**   **voltage**

Paddles are placed on the patient's ____**1**____ . They must make a good ____**2**____ contact with the body. To make the heart ____**3**____ electric ____**4**____ is passed through the body. No-one must touch the person so they do not get an electric ____**5**____ .   **[5]**

7. Sadia has bought a new electric lamp. It is **double insulated** so it does not need **earthing**.
  (a) What does double insulated mean?   **[1]**
  (b) The lamp has a 3 A fuse. Describe what happens when:
       (i) The normal current of 0.25 A flows in the circuit
       (ii) There is a fault and the current increases to 5 A.   **[2]**
  (c) The fault is fixed and the fuse is replaced with a 13 A fuse. Explain why this is not a good idea.   **[1]**

8. Tom works at a car body shop. He spray paints the cars.
  The spray gun is charged so that the **paint droplets** are all **positively charged**.
  (a) What effect does this have on the paint spray?   **[2]**
  (b) The car body is charged with the **opposite charge** to the paint droplets. Why is this?   **[1]**
  (c) Describe two advantages of charging the paint spray and the car body   **[2]**

9. Ali is investigating how the current through a diode depends on the potential difference.

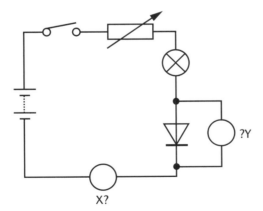

  (a) Complete the circuit to show where the ammeter and the voltmeter should be placed in the circuit.   **[2]**

Exam practice questions

He plots this graph for the diode to show how the current varies with potential difference.

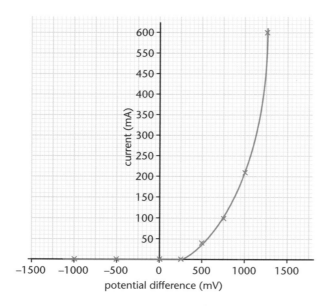

The lamp has a normal operating current of 250 mA. At this current it has a normal brightness.

(b) What is the potential difference that gives a current of 250 mA? [1]

(c) Describe how the brightness is changed when the potential difference is
   (i) 1200 mV
   (ii) – 1200 mV
   (iii) 500 mV [3]

(d) Ali replaces the battery with an a.c. power supply. How is an a.c. supply different from a d.c. supply? [2]

(e) Explain what will happen to the current now that there is an a.c. supply and a diode in the circuit. [2]

Waves and radiation

The following topics are covered in this chapter:

- **Describing waves**
- **Sound and ultrasound**
- **Wave properties**
- **Electromagnetic waves**

11.1 Describing waves

Types of wave

 OCR A   **P6.1**

OCR B   **P4d**

A **wave** is a **vibration** or disturbance which is transmitted through a material – called a **medium** – or through space. Waves transfer **energy** and can also be used to transfer **information** from one place to another, but they do not transfer material.

> A common mistake is to mark the amplitude from the top of a peak to the bottom of a trough – this is twice the amplitude.

Transverse waves

A **transverse wave** has the vibrations at **right angles** (perpendicular) to the direction of wave travel. The wave has **peaks** (or **crests**) and **troughs**, as shown in Fig. 11.1. The **amplitude** is the maximum displacement (change in position) from the undisturbed position. The **wavelength** (symbol λ) is the distance between two neighbouring peaks or troughs.

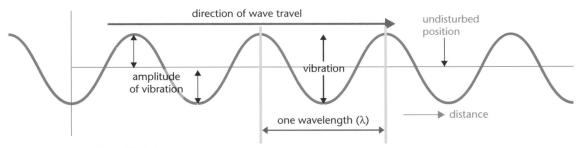

Fig. 11.1 A transverse wave.

The **frequency** is the number of complete waves that pass through a point in one second. It depends on how fast the source of the waves is vibrating. The frequency is measured in **hertz** (Hz) where one hertz is one cycle (wave) per second.

The **wave speed** depends on the medium that the wave is travelling through. As the frequency increases the wave speed does not change, but the wavelength will decrease. This is shown in Fig. 11.2.

Fig. 11.2 Waves with different frequency and wavelength.

The **wave equation** relates the wavelength and frequency to the wave speed.

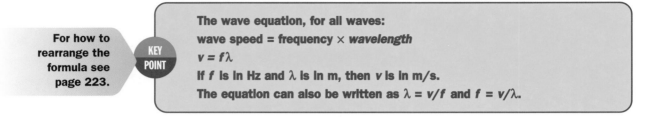

For how to rearrange the formula see page 223.

KEY POINT

The wave equation, for all waves:
wave speed = frequency × *wavelength*
$v = f\lambda$
If f is in Hz and λ is in m, then v is in m/s.
The equation can also be written as $\lambda = v/f$ and $f = v/\lambda$.

Examples of transverse waves are: water waves, light and other electromagnetic waves, and the seismic waves called S-waves.

Longitudinal waves

OCR A   P6.1
OCR B   P4d

A **longitudinal wave** has the vibrations **parallel** to (along the same direction as) the direction of the wave travel. As shown in the diagram, the wave has **compressions** (or squashed parts) and between these are stretched parts called **rarefactions**.

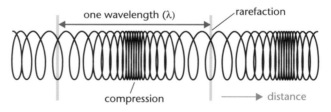

Fig. 11.3 A longitudinal wave.

One wavelength is the length of one complete wave – a compression and a rarefaction. Longitudinal waves show the same behaviour (for example, reflection and refraction) as transverse waves.

Motion of particles in waves

OCR A   P6.1
OCR B   P4d

When a wave travels through a **medium**, the particles move backwards and forwards about their normal position – they **oscillate**. Figure 11.4 shows this for a transverse and a longitudinal wave.
The **wavelength** is the distance between any particle and the next particle that is at the same stage in its oscillation.

Fig. 11.4 Movement of the particles as a wave passes.

11.2 Sound and ultrasound

Sound waves and electromagnetic waves – the differences

OCR A **P6.3**

> **You will not be expected to remember the speed of electromagnetic waves in the exam.**

Sound waves	Electromagnetic waves
longitudinal waves	transverse waves
cannot travel through empty space (a vacuum)	can travel through empty space (a vacuum)
can travel through solids, liquids and gases	can travel through some solids, liquids and gases
oscillations (movement back and forth) of the particles in the medium	oscillations (movement from side to side) of electric and magnetic fields
travel about a million times slower than electromagnetic waves in air	travel at 300 000 km/s in a vacuum, very slightly slower in air

Ultrasound

OCR B **P4d**

Ultrasound waves are sound waves with a **frequency** that is too high for humans to hear. The frequency is above the **upper threshold** of human hearing.

Ultrasound is also used to **scan** parts of the body, like the eye or an unborn fetus. This works because part of the pulse is reflected at each **boundary between** different layers of tissue. The reflections from the tissue boundaries are all used to build up a picture.

Ultrasound scans have two advantages over X-ray scans:
- ultrasound does not damage living cells or DNA and does not cause mutation
- ultrasound can produce images of soft tissue.

Ultrasound is also used to break down stones such as kidney stones or gall stones. The vibrations caused by the ultrasound make the stone break down.

11.3 Wave properties

Absorption, emission and reflection

OCR A   P6.2

All surfaces **emit** electromagnetic radiation that depends on their **temperature**. They also **transmit**, **absorb** and/or **reflect** some of the radiation that falls on them. How much is transmitted, how much absorbed and how much reflected depends on the surface. Reflection happens to waves and particles. If a wave, or a ball, strikes a wall at an angle it will be reflected so that the **angle of incidence** is equal to the **angle of reflection**.

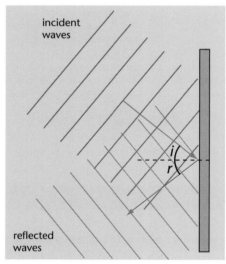
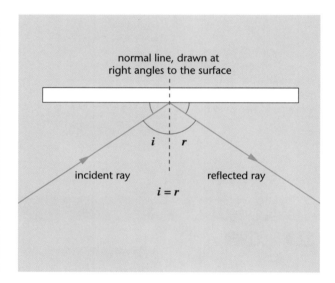

Fig. 11.5 Reflection.

Refraction

OCR A   P6.2

When waves enter a **denser medium**, they slow down. When they enter a less dense medium, they speed up. In both cases, this may cause them to **change direction**. This happens to water waves but also to particles, as you can show by rolling a ball at an angle down a ramp. When the slope of the ramp changes the direction of the ball changes.

Water waves slow down as they go from deep water to shallow water.

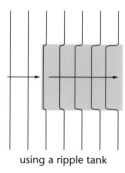

using a ripple tank

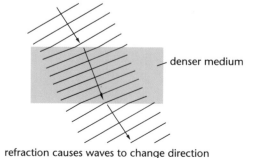

denser medium

refraction causes waves to change direction

Fig. 11.6 Refraction.

Diffraction

OCR A P6.2

Diffraction is the **spreading** out of a wave when it passes through a gap. The effect is most noticeable when the gap is the same size as the wavelength. Particles cannot be diffracted. So diffraction is good evidence for a wave.

> When answering questions it is important to say that the amount of spreading depends on the size of the gap compared with the wavelength.

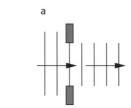 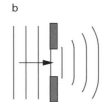 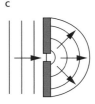

a   b   c

Fig. 11.7 Diffraction.

Interference

OCR A P6.2

Interference occurs where two waves overlap. If the waves have the same **amplitude** and **wavelength** and are in **phase** (in step), they can **interfere**. Fig. 11.8 shows that if the crests arrive **together** there will be **constructive** interference and the amplitude will **increase**. If a crest arrives at the same time as a trough the two will **cancel** out and there is no wave. This is **destructive** interference. Particles cannot interfere, so interference is good evidence for a wave.

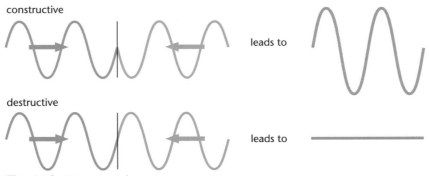

constructive

leads to

destructive

leads to

Fig. 11.8 Wave interference.

Total internal reflection

OCR A P6.2

Total internal reflection can only happen when light travels from a **dense to a less dense medium** – for example from glass to air. If the angle of incidence is so large that the angle of refraction would be greater then 90° then it is impossible for the light to leave the glass – so total internal reflection occurs.

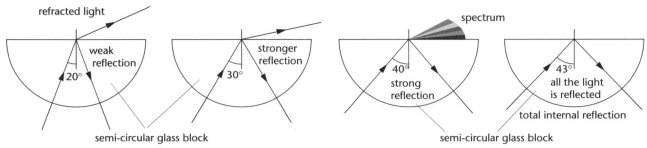

Fig. 11.9 When air meets an air–glass boundary.

Transparent materials have a **critical angle**. When the angle of incidence equals the critical angle, the angle of refraction is 90°. At angles greater than the critical angle, total internal reflection occurs. The critical angle for a glass–air boundary is about 42°. Total internal reflection can also occur at a Perspex–air boundary and at a water–air boundary.

More about light and sound

OCR A   P6.2

These 'More about' sections build on earlier 'Wave properties' sections.

Reflection

Sound can be reflected, and the **angle of incidence** equals the **angle of reflection** as shown on page 196. Reflections of sound waves are called **echoes**.

Refraction

When the **speed** of a wave changes, there is a change in the **wavelength**, because there is no change in the **frequency**. This can cause a change in direction as shown on page 194. Light travels more slowly in glass than in air, so a light ray is refracted as it passes through a glass block as shown in Fig. 11.10.

Sound is refracted, for example, in a different gas. Fig. 11.11 shows how a balloon full of **carbon dioxide** will **refract** sound waves (they travel more slowly in carbon dioxide than in air). More sound reaches the ear with the balloon in place than without the balloon.

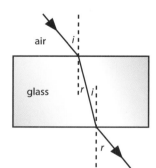

Fig. 11.10 Refraction of light in a glass block.

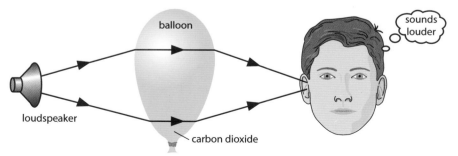

Fig. 11.11 Refraction of sound through a balloon filled with carbon dioxide.

More about light and sound – Diffraction

OCR A   P6.2

> **KEY POINT**
>
> For diffraction to occur at all, the gap must be of a similar size to the wavelength of the wave.

The wavelength of sound is about a metre, so it is diffracted through doorways. (It is also reflected off walls, so hearing around a corner is partly due to diffraction, and partly reflection.) For light to be diffracted, the gap size must be about a thousandth of a millimetre – because the wavelength of light is so small. Patterns caused by diffraction of light can be seen through materials with a fine mesh, for example, a street lamp seen through a net curtain.

More about light and sound – Interference

OCR A   P6.2

When identical sound waves from two speakers meet, there are positions where the waves arriving reinforce and give louder sound, and other positions where the waves cancel out to give a quiet point. Fig. 11.12 shows the pattern of loud and quiet areas.

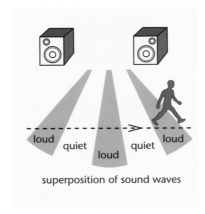

Fig. 11.12 Interference of sound waves.

A famous example of an **interference pattern** formed by light waves is called Young's experiment. Fig 11.13 shows how two very narrow slits close together are illuminated and the **diffracted light** from each slit overlaps and produces an interference pattern of **bright** and **dark lines**.

To see the pattern, the slits must be about a thousandth of a millimetre wide, and only about half a millimetre apart.

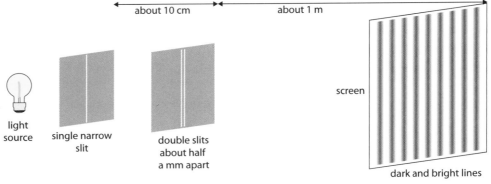

Fig. 11.13 Young's experiment – an interference pattern.

Evidence that light and sound are waves

OCR A   P6.2

Particles can be reflected. For example, on a snooker or pool table a ball striking the cushion bounces off so that the angle of incidence equals the angle of refraction.

Particles can be refracted. For example, if a ball rolls along a flat surface towards a ramp, but not at right angles to the ramp, when it reaches the ramp it will change direction. Fig. 11.14 shows the path of the ball.

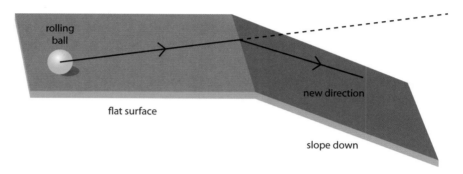

rolling ball

new direction

flat surface

slope down

Fig. 11.14 A ball changes direction as it speeds up rolling down a ramp.

> **KEY POINT** Particles cannot be diffracted, or show interference effects. These properties are evidence of wave behaviour.

Property	Light?	Evidence that light is a wave?	Sound?	Evidence that sound is a wave?
reflection	yes	no – could be a particle	yes	no – could be a particle
refraction	yes	no – could be a particle	yes	no – could be a particle
diffraction	yes	yes	yes	yes
interference	yes	yes	yes	yes

11.4 Electromagnetic waves

Frequency and energy

OCR A   P6.3

The spectrum of electromagnetic waves is continuous from the **longest** wavelengths (**radio waves**) through to the **shortest** wavelengths (**gamma rays**). These **wavelengths** are related to the **frequencies** using the wave equation – radio waves have the lowest frequency and gamma rays the highest. The **higher** the **frequency**, the more **energy** the waves have.

Fig. 11.15 shows the spectrum, from left to right, in order of increasing frequency and energy, from right to left in order of increasing wavelength.

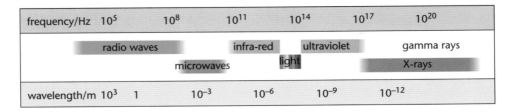

frequency/Hz	10^5		10^8		10^{11}		10^{14}		10^{17}		10^{20}
			radio waves				infra-red		ultraviolet		gamma rays
					microwaves			light			X-rays
wavelength/m	10^3	1			10^{-3}		10^{-6}		10^{-9}		10^{-12}

Fig. 11.15 The electromagnetic spectrum.

The photon model

OCR A **P6.3**

Electromagnetic radiation can be described as packets of **energy** called **photons**.

> **KEY POINT**
> The energy delivered by each photon in a beam of electromagnetic radiation increases with the frequency of the radiation.

For example, a gamma ray photon has a higher frequency, and photon energy than a microwave photon.

The **intensity** of a beam of electromagnetic radiation is the **energy** it delivers each second. The intensity depends on the **number of photons** arriving each second, and the **energy** carried by **each photon**.

X-rays and gamma rays

OCR A **P6.3,4**
OCR B **P4e**
EDEXCEL 360 **P2.11**

The uses of X-rays and gamma rays are covered in 12.1 Uses of radioactivity.

The difference between gamma rays and X-rays is in the way they are produced. **Gamma rays** come from the nucleus of some radioactive atoms. **X-rays** are produced by firing high speed electrons at a metal target in an X-ray machine. X-rays are easier to control than gamma rays. **X-rays** are used for:

- **Medical scans**, for example to show broken bones. They pass through the body tissues but are stopped by denser materials such as the bones, which show up as shadows on film or a screen.
- **Security scans** of passengers' luggage. They pass through the suitcase and clothes, but metal items and batteries stop the X-rays and show up as shadows on the screen.

Radio waves

OCR A **P6.3**

Radio waves are the lowest-energy, lowest-frequency and longest-wavelength electromagnetic waves. They are produced when an **alternating current** flows in an **aerial** and they spread out and travel through the atmosphere. They are not strongly absorbed by the atmosphere. Another aerial is used as a detector and the waves produce an alternating current in it, with a frequency that matches that of the radio waves. Anyone with a receiver can tune it to this

A common mistake is to think that we can hear radio waves. We cannot hear any electromagnetic radiation. The radiation is used to carry a signal that is converted into a sound wave by the receiver.

frequency to pick up the **radio waves** so they are suitable for **broadcasting** (for example, radio and TV programmes) to large numbers of people. An advantage is that this method of communicating does not require wires to transmit information. A disadvantage is that radio stations using similar transmission frequencies sometimes **interfere**.

Medium wavelength radio waves are **reflected** from the **ionosphere**, a layer of charged particles in the upper atmosphere, so they can be used for long distance communication.

Digital radio has better-quality reception as it uses digital signals and so does not have problems of noise and interference.

Microwaves

Microwaves are sometimes considered to be **very short radio waves** (high-frequency and high-energy radio waves).

Some important properties of microwaves are:
- They are **reflected** by **metal** surfaces.
- They **heat materials** if they can make **atoms** or **molecules** in the material **vibrate**. The amount of heating depends on the **intensity** of the microwave radiation, and the **time** that the material is exposed to the radiation.
- They pass through **glass and plastics**.
- They pass through the **atmosphere**.
- They pass through the **ionosphere** without being reflected.
- They are **absorbed by water molecules**, how well depends on the frequency (energy) of the microwaves.
- Transmission is affected by wave effects such as reflection, refraction, diffraction and interference.

Microwaves and water molecules

A **microwave** frequency (energy) can be selected which is strongly absorbed by **water molecules**, causing them to **vibrate**, and increasing their **kinetic energy**. This effect can be used to heat materials containing water, for example **food**. If the most strongly absorbed frequency (energy) is used in a **microwave oven** it only cooks the outside of the food because it is all absorbed before it penetrates the food. So the frequency (energy) used in a microwave oven is changed slightly to one that will **penetrate** about **1 cm** into the food. Conduction and convection processes then spread the heat through the food.

As our **bodies** contain water molecules in our **cells**, microwave oven radiation will heat up our cells and is very **dangerous at high intensity** because it will burn body tissue. The radiation is kept inside the oven by the **reflecting metal case** and **metal grid** in the door.

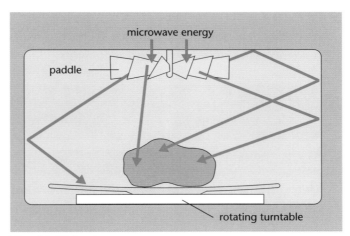

Fig. 11.16 A microwave oven.

Microwaves sent through the **atmosphere** will be absorbed by water so they can be used to **monitor rain**. The weaker the signal reaching the detector, the more rain the microwaves have passed through.

Microwave transmissions

Wireless technology uses **microwaves** and **radio waves** to transmit **information**. Advantages are:

- we can receive phone calls and email 24 hours a day
- no wiring is needed to connect laptops to the Internet, or for mobile phones or radio
- communication with wireless technology is portable and convenient.

Microwaves can be used to **transmit signals** over large distances if there are no obstacles between to reflect or absorb the beam. Another way to say this is that the transmitter and receiver are in **line of sight** (one can be seen from the other). This is why the transmitters are positioned high up, often on tall microwave masts. They cannot be spaced so far apart that, for example, hills or the curvature of the Earth stop the beam.

Microwaves are used to send signals to and from **satellites**. The satellites can relay signals around the Earth. Microwaves are used because they pass through the atmosphere and through the ionosphere. The signals may be for television programmes, telephone conversations, or monitoring the Earth (for example, weather forecasting).

When microwaves are transmitted from a dish the wavelength must be small compared to the dish diameter to reduce diffraction – the spreading out of the beam. The dish is made of metal because metal reflects microwaves well.

Mobile phones use microwave signals. The signals from the transmitting phones reflect off metal surfaces and walls to communicate with the nearest transmitter mast. There is a network of transmitter masts to relay the signals on to the nearest mast to the receiving phone.

Mobile phones have not been in widespread use for many years, so there is not much data about the possible **dangers** of using them. The transmitter is held close to the user's head so the microwaves must have a small heating effect on the brain. There are questions about whether this could be dangerous, or whether it is not large enough to be a problem. So far studies have not found that users have suffered any serious ill effects. There may also be a risk to residents living close to mobile phone masts.

> **KEY POINT** Low-intensity microwave radiation, from mobile phone masts and hand-sets, may be a health risk, but there is disagreement about this.

Digital and analogue signals

Electromagnetic radiation is used for **communications** and **transmission of information**. The waves that are used in this way are **radio waves**, **microwaves**, **infrared radiation** and **light**.

The idea of using a signal lamp to communicate was used in the 19th century. This method of long distance communication needed a code. One code used was **Morse code**, a series of long and short flashes of light for different letters of the alphabet. These signals can only be seen when visibility is good and for short distances.

Today we still use codes to send signals using electromagnetic radiation. There are two types of signal, **analogue** and **digital**. An analogue signal changes in frequency and amplitude all the time in a way that matches the changes in the voice or music being transmitted. A digital signal has just two values – which we can represent as **0 and 1**.

> **KEY POINT** An analogue signal varies in frequency and amplitude. A digital signal has two values, 0 and 1 (or 'on' and 'off').

The signal (voice, music or data) is converted into a code using only the values 0 and 1. The signal becomes a stream of 0 and 1 values. These pulses are added to the electromagnetic wave and transmitted. The signal is received and then decoded to recover the original signal.

Both analogue and digital signals can pick up unwanted signals that distort the original signal. These **unwanted signals** are called **noise**. Digital signals can be cleaned up in a process known as **regeneration** because each pulse must be a 0 or a 1, so other values can be removed. Analogue signals can be **amplified**, but the noise is amplified too. This is why digital signals give a better-quality reception.

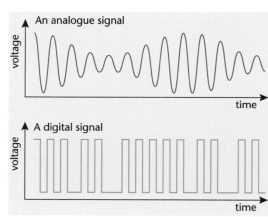

Fig. 11.17 How analogue and digital signals change with time.

> **KEY POINT** Digital signals give a better-quality reception because noise on digital signals is more easily removed.

Communications using infrared radiation and light

OCR A **P6.4**

Infrared radiation and **light** travel along **glass optical fibres** by being **totally internally reflected**. The fibres are made with a core that has a different refractive index from that of the outer rim. The signal is reflected at the boundary as shown in Fig. 11.18.

Signals (**pulses of radiation**) can be sent for long distances using **optical fibres**. A stream of data can be transmitted very quickly. There is **less interference** than with microwaves passing through the atmosphere. It is also possible to use **multiplexing**, a way of sending many different signals down one fibre at the same time. Digital signals are used so that noise can be removed when the signal is regenerated.

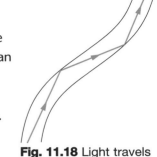

Fig. 11.18 Light travels along optical fibres.

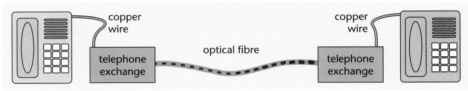

Fig. 11.19 Modern phones use optical fibres.

Modulation

OCR A **P6.4**

To communicate information, for example music or data, the information must be added to the light or radio wave. For example, these are the steps to broadcast music using analogue radio:

- A microphone is used to produce an electrical signal that matches the music (an analogue signal). This is called an **audio frequency (AF) signal**
- A radio wave frequency band (small range of radio frequencies) is chosen to carry the signal. This is called a **radio frequency (RF) carrier**
- The **AF signal** is added to the **RF carrier** in a process called **modulation** (The AF signal is used to modulate the RF carrier)
- The modulated radio wave is broadcast from a transmitter aerial
- The radio receiver aerial receives all the transmitted radio waves. Its job is to reproduce the original sound – the music. You tune the radio receiver to the **RF carrier** you want – the one used by the radio station broadcasting the music
- The modulated radio wave is received and demodulated to remove the **RF carrier** from the **AF signal**
- The **AF signal** will have decreased in intensity and needs amplifying. It is amplified and sent to the loudspeaker.

Amplitude modulation and frequency modulation

> There are two types of modulation. In amplitude modulation (AM) the amplitude of the radio wave is varied to match the audio frequency (AF) signal. In frequency modulation (FM) the frequency of the radio wave is varied to match the audio frequency (AF) signal.

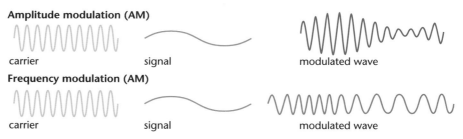

Amplitude modulation (AM)

carrier   signal   modulated wave

Frequency modulation (AM)

carrier   signal   modulated wave

Fig. 11.20 Amplitude modulation (AM) and frequency modulation (FM)

As the signal travels it picks up random additional signals – called **noise**. This reduces the quality of the signal. When the signal is amplified the noise is amplified too, as shown in Fig. 11.21 below. The amplitude is more affected by noise than the frequency, so **FM** broadcasts are **less affected** by **noise** than **AM** broadcasts.

Digital signals

Digital radio has an extra step involved. The AF signal is converted to a **digital AF signal** which is then used to modulate the radio frequency (RF) carrier wave. The digital AF signal must be decoded in the radio receiver before it is sent to the loudspeaker. The advantage, shown in Fig. 11.21, is that the 'on' and 'off' states can still be recognised despite any **noise** that is picked up. The signal can be 'cleaned up' to remove any noise so digital signals can be **regenerated** and give higher quality reception.

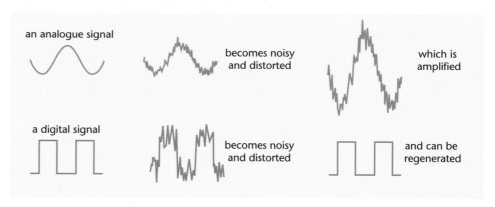

an analogue signal   becomes noisy and distorted   which is amplified

a digital signal   becomes noisy and distorted   and can be regenerated

Fig. 11.21 Digital transmission can have higher quality.

HOW SCIENCE WORKS

What is light?

The boxes A to H describe the stages in the development of scientists' theories about light. Box A is the first box. Read them all and see if you can decide the correct order for the others.

Box A

If it is completely dark and you have a searchlight you can move it around and pick out objects that you can see in the light beam. Most children begin with this idea of how the eye works – it sends out a ray to see things. It is possible this was the earliest idea of how light behaved.

Fig. 11.22 Seeing an object?

Box B

In 1704, Isaac Newton did some experiments with light. He knew that waves were diffracted when they passed through small gaps. He checked very carefully and could see no evidence that light was diffracted. He said light must be a stream of particles.

Fig. 11.23 Shadows have sharp edges.

Box C

In 1905, Albert Einstein published his theory that light behaves as a beam of particles called photons. He used this theory to explain why high frequency light caused electrons to be emitted from the surface of some metals when low frequency light did not – no matter how much you turned up the intensity of the light.

Box D

About 2500 years ago, the Ancient Greeks suggested a theory that light was a stream of particles, for example from the Sun or a lamp. When the particles bounced off objects the light was reflected. When people saw objects it was because the light particles had entered their eyes.

HOW SCIENCE WORKS

Box E

Today scientists have accepted that sometimes light behaves as a wave and sometimes it behaves as a particle. They use a wave theory of light or a particle theory of light depending on which is best suited to the situation they are trying to explain.

Box F

In the fifteenth century Leonardo da Vinci compared reflections of light to echoes of sound. As sound was considered to be a wave, this suggested that light was also a wave.

Box G

Thomas Young's ideas were accepted in other parts of Europe before they were accepted in the United Kingdom because British scientists had such a high opinion of Isaac Newton, they did not believe his ideas could be wrong.

Box H

In 1802, Thomas Young showed that – with small enough gaps – light does show diffraction and interference effects that can only be explained by a wave theory. The gaps had to be about the width of a hair because the wavelength of light is so small.

1. What is the correct order of the boxes? **[4]**

2. There are several reasons why scientists sometimes find it difficult to accept new explanations. Why did some UK scientists find it difficult to accept that light was a wave? **[1]**

3. Today scientists say that light is a beam of particles called photons. Does this mean that Thomas Young was wrong to say that light was a wave? Explain your answer. **[2]**

Exam practice questions

1. Which word describes the number of waves passing a point in one second?

   A   amplitude

   B   frequency

   C   wavelength

   D   wave speed   [1]

2. The diagram shows how water waves spread out after passing through a gap.
   This effect is called:

   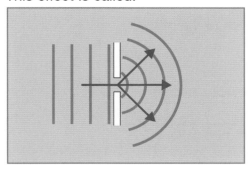

   A   diffraction

   B   dispersion

   C   reflection

   D   refraction   [1]

3. A digital signal can be transmitted with higher quality than an analogue signal because:

   A   The radio wave does not have to be modulated.

   B   The digital signal does not pick up so much noise.

   C   The digital signal does not need to be amplified.

   D   The digital signal can be cleaned up and then amplified.   [1]

4. Some ocean waves have a wavelength of 200 m and 1 wave passes a rock every
   10 seconds. The distance from the top of a crest to the bottom of a trough is 4 m.

   Tick ✔ **true** or **false** for each statement.

	True	False
The frequency of the waves is 10 Hz		
The wave speed is 20 m/s		
The waves are transverse waves		
The amplitude is 2 m		

   [4]

Exam practice questions

5. Choose words from the list to complete this description of how radio waves can be used to broadcast a TV programme. (Use words once, more than once, or not at all.)

**aerial   analogue   carrier   demodulated
digital   modulate   signal   transmitter**

The TV signal is used to _____1_____ the radio frequency _____2_____ wave. The radio wave is broadcast from the _____3_____ aerial. The receiver _____4_____ picks up the broadcast _____5_____. The radio wave is _____6_____ to recover the TV signal.   **[6]**

6. Draw lines to join the range of electromagnetic waves to the use.

Range   **Use**

| microwaves | | communication with satellites |

| radio waves | | optical fibre communications |

| infrared | | medical scans |

| x-rays | | TV broadcasts | **[3]**

7. **(a)** What is ultrasound?

(b) Ultrasound is used to build up an image of the unborn fetus. Explain what happens to the ultrasound when it reaches the fetus.

(c) State another medical use, other than scanning parts of the body, of ultrasound.   **[4]**

8. **(a)** Complete the labels to describe the sound wave shown in the diagram below.

A _____

B _____

C _____

D _____ wave

(b) A transverse wave moves from left to right across the water. Describe how the particles move as the wave passes.   **[6]**

Nuclear physics

The following topics are covered in this chapter:

- **Radioactivity**
- **Atomic structure**
- **Changes in the nucleus**
- **Nuclear reactors**

12.1 Radioactivity

Alpha, beta and gamma radiation

A **radioactive nucleus** is **unstable** and will emit radiation. There are three main types:

- **Alpha (α)** is strongly ionising radiation, but it only travels a few centimetres in air and is stopped by a thin sheet of paper.
- **Beta (β)** is ionising radiation that penetrates card or several sheets of paper, but is stopped by a 3 mm thick sheet of aluminium or other metal.
- **Gamma (γ)** is weakly ionising radiation that is very penetrating. It is reduced significantly by a thick lead sheet or blocks of concrete.

> **KEY POINT**
>
> There are three types of radioactive emissions: alpha, beta and gamma radiation. Alpha radiation is the most ionising, gamma radiation is the most penetrating.

Alpha and **beta** radiation is deflected by **magnetic fields** and **electric fields**, but **gamma** radiation is not affected.

Background radiation

Radioactive materials occur naturally, and can also be made artificially. **Cosmic rays** from space make some of the carbon dioxide in the atmosphere radioactive. The carbon dioxide is used by plants and enters food chains. This makes all living things radioactive. Some rocks are also radioactive.

Background radiation is radioactive emissions from nuclei in our surroundings. Do not confuse this with radiation from other sources, such as radiation from mobile phones.

We receive a low level of radiation from these sources all the time. It is called **background radiation.** Background radiation comes from:

- space (cosmic rays) and the Sun
- building materials, rocks (e.g. granite) and soil
- radioactive nuclei in all plants and animals
- medical and industrial uses of radioactive materials
- 'leaks' from radioactive waste and nuclear power stations.

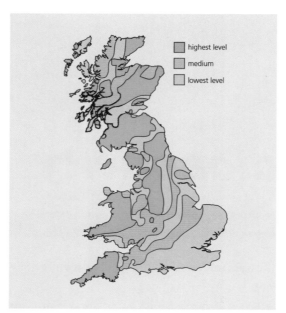

Fig. 12.1 In some parts of the country the rocks are more radioactive than in others and there is a higher level of background radiation.

highest level
medium
lowest level

Ionising radiation

EDEXCEL 360 P2.11

> Gamma rays, X-rays and ultra-violet radiation are the three types of electromagnetic radiation with high enough frequency to cause ionisation.

Ionising radiation is radiation that has enough energy to break molecules or atoms into charged particles called **ions**. The molecules or atoms lose **electrons** in a process called **ionisation**. The ions can then take part in chemical reactions. This is how ionising radiation damages **living cells**. It kills them, or damages the **DNA** in the cell so that the cell **mutates** (changes) into a **cancer** cell, which then grows in an uncontrolled manner.

Ionising radiation includes alpha, beta and gamma radiation from the radioactive nuclei and also X-rays and ultra-violet radiation.

Of the radioactive emissions, alpha particles are the most ionising, followed by beta particles, and gamma rays are the least ionising.

> Make sure you know the difference.

Contamination or irradiation?

If a person has a radioactive material on their skin or clothes, or has swallowed or inhaled it, this is called **radioactive contamination**. The radioactive material will decay over a period of time. This results in a higher dose of radiation than being exposed to an external source, which is called **irradiation**, because when the person moves away from the source they are no longer irradiated. This is especially true of the most ionising radiation, alpha radiation. Unlike beta and gamma radiation, alpha radiation cannot penetrate the skin, so outside the body – a few centimetres away – it is not dangerous. But if a person inhales, or swallows, material that emits alpha particles, the source will continue to emit them inside the body until all the radioactive nuclei have decayed. This increases the risk of cancer.

Risk and safety

EDEXCEL 360 P2.11

It is **not possible to predict** which cells will be damaged by exposure to radiation, and it is not possible to say who will get cancer. Scientists have studied the survivors of incidents where people have been exposed to ionising radiation. They measured the amount of exposure and recorded how many people later suffered from cancer.

They introduced **radiation dose**, measured in **sieverts**, which is a measure of the **possible harm done to the body**. Radiation dose depends on the **type of radiation**, the **time of exposure** and how **sensitive the tissue** exposed is to radiation. Scientists can then give a figure for the **risk** of cancer developing.

To reduce the risk to living cells, radioactive materials must be handled **safely**:

- wear protective clothing
- keep a long distance away (use tongs to handle sources)
- keep the exposure time short
- sources should be shielded and labelled with the radioactive symbol.

Fig. 12.2 Radioactive hazard symbol.

These precautions keep the dose as low as possible. Radioactive materials are used, for example, in hospitals and nuclear power stations. Employers must keep the dose for their employees **as low as reasonably achievable**: this is known as the **alara** principle.

You may have had an X-ray photograph taken and noticed that the staff move behind a screen or out of the room, so that they are not exposed to X-rays every time the X-ray machine is used. Employees at nuclear power stations, and other places where nuclear sources are used, may wear a **film badge** to monitor the exposure to radiation. Airline employees working as flight crew are monitored too, because the exposure to cosmic rays is increased if you fly at high altitudes in the thin atmosphere of the Earth.

Uses of radioactive sources

OCR B   P4e
EDEXCEL 360 P2.11

For each use:

- the radiation is chosen depending on the range and the absorption (see 12.1 Alpha, beta and gamma radiation)
- the source is chosen depending on how long it will remain radioactive (see 12.4 Radioactive decay and Half-life).

Medical and health uses

OCR B   P 4e
EDEXCEL 360 P2.11

Medical tracers

Sources which emit **gamma radiation** are used in **medical tracers**. The patient drinks, inhales, or is injected with the tracer which is chosen to target the organ doctors want to examine. For example, radioactive iodine is taken up

by the thyroid gland, which can then be viewed using a **gamma camera** that detects the gamma radiation passing out of the body. The tracer must not decay before it has moved to the organ being investigated but it must not last so long that the patient stays radioactive for weeks afterwards. Sources which emit a higher dose of **gamma radiation** are used in the same way for **treating cancer** by building up in the cancer and killing the cancer cells.

Treating cancer

A beam of gamma rays is directed at a cancer to kill the cancer cells. One source used for this is cobalt-60. It emits high energy gamma rays and remains radioactive for years.

Sterilisation

Sources which emit **gamma radiation** are used to produce a beam of gamma rays that will:

- **sterilise equipment**, such as surgical instruments, by destroying microbes
- extend the shelf-life of perishable **food**, by destroying microbes.

The food and equipment does not become radioactive because it is only **irradiated**. It does not touch the radioactive material, so there is no **contamination**.

Smoke detectors

OCR B   P 4g
EDEXCEL 360   P2.11

Sources which emit **alpha radiation** are used in **smoke detectors**. The alpha radiation from the source ionises the air and the ions cross a small gap and are picked up by a detector. If smoke is present the alpha radiation is stopped by the smoke particles. No ions reach the detector and an alarm is sounded.

Beta and gamma radiation are unsuitable because they pass through the smoke.

Tracers

OCR B   P 4g

Tracers that emit **beta radiation** are added to liquid waste at a factory or to sewage and then samples of water are taken from different places in a river to find out if the waste is entering the river. The **radioisotope** that is used has a half-life of hours or days so that it soon decays and does not contaminate the environment.

Tracers that emit **gamma radiation** can be used to find the routes of underground pipes, or leaks or blockages in pipes, as shown in Fig. 12.3. Gamma radiation is used so that it will reach the surface, and half-lives of days or hours are used to avoid contamination of the environment.

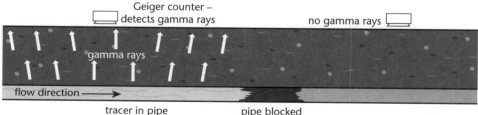

Fig. 12.3

12.2 *Atomic structure*

A model of the atom

AQA   P2.13.9

Before 1910 scientists had a **plum pudding** model of the **atom**. They imagined that the atom was made of positively charged material (the pudding) with the negatively charged electrons distributed inside it (the plums). Ernest Rutherford realised that **alpha particles** were smaller than atoms and thought up an experiment to find out more about the structure of atoms. Alpha particles were fired at a very thin sheet of **gold foil**, rolled out to be just a few atoms thick. The experiment was done in a vacuum, so that the alpha particles were not stopped by the air. It was surrounded by a screen made of fluorescent material, so that a small flash of light was seen when an alpha particle hit the screen. Hans Geiger and Ernest Marsden did the experiment – they counted small flashes of light at different angles for hours. The table shows their observations.

What happened to the alpha particles	Ernest Rutherford's explanation
Most went straight through the foil, without being deflected	The atom is mostly empty space
Some were deflected, and there was a range deflection angles	Some passed closer to charged parts of the atom
A small number were 'back-scattered' – they came straight back towards the alpha particle source	There are tiny regions of concentrated positive charge which repel the small number of alpha particles that have a head-on collision

> Rutherford said the back-scattering surprised him – it was as if you fired a gun at a piece of tissue paper and the bullet came back at you.

Fig. 12.4 shows how this model accounts for the observations.

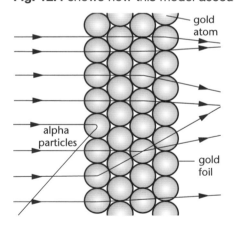

This lead to our 'solar system' or **nuclear model** of the atom.
- The atom has a central nucleus where most of the mass is concentrated. It is positively charged.
- The nucleus is very small compared to the volume, or shell, around the nucleus that contains the electrons.

Different atoms

AQA   P2.13.9
EDEXCEL 360   P2.11

This table summarises the properties of the particles found in the atom. The values for relative mass and the relative charge give a comparison of the particles.

The protons and neutrons are collectively called nucleons.

Particle	Symbol	Where found in the atom	Relative mass	Relative charge
proton	p	in nucleus	1	+1
neutron	n	in nucleus	1	0 (neutral)
electron	e	outside nucleus	$\dfrac{1}{1840}$	−1

> **KEY POINT**
> The atomic number or proton number, **Z**, is the number of protons in the nucleus. Atoms of different elements have different numbers of protons.

> **KEY POINT**
> The mass number or nucleon number, **A**, is the total number of protons and neutrons in the nucleus. Atoms of the same element with different numbers of neutrons are called isotopes.

The nucleus is given a symbol $^{A}_{Z}$El where A is mass number Z is the proton number and El is the chemical symbol for the element. For example $^{12}_{6}$C is a stable isotope of carbon with 6 protons and 6 neutrons.

12.3 Changes in the nucleus

Radioactive decay

OCR B   P 4f
AQA   P2.13.9
EDEXCEL 360   P2.11

A radioactive nucleus is unstable and emits nuclear radiation. This process is called **radioactive decay**. It is not possible to predict when this will happen, nor is it possible to make it happen by a chemical or physical process, (for example by heating it). The **decay** is **random**.

Radioactive emissions

OCR B   P 4f
AQA   P2.13.9

Alpha emission is when **two protons and two neutrons** leave the nucleus as one particle. This alpha particle is identical to a helium nucleus so has the symbol: $^{4}_{2}$He. The new nucleus has a mass number which has decreased by four and an atomic number which has decreased by 2. For example radon –220 is a gas that decays by alpha emission.

$$^{220}_{86}Rn \rightarrow \; ^{216}_{84}Po + \; ^{4}_{2}He$$

Beta emission occurs when a **neutron** decays to a **proton** and an **electron** and the electron leaves the nucleus. The atomic number increases by one and the mass number is unchanged. The beta particle is a high energy electron and has the symbol: $^{0}_{-1}e$

$^{14}_{6}C$ is a radioactive isotope of carbon with 6 protons and 8 neutrons.

This nucleus emits beta radiation and forms a nitrogen nucleus:

$$^{14}_{6}C \rightarrow \; ^{14}_{7}N + \; ^{0}_{-1}e$$

> **A beta particle is an electron from the nucleus – not an orbital electron.**

Gamma emission occurs when the nucleus emits a short burst of high energy electromagnetic radiation. The gamma ray has a high frequency and a short wavelength.

> **KEY POINT**
>
> alpha particle: a helium nucleus $^{4}_{2}He$
> beta particle: high-energy electron $^{0}_{-1}e$
> gamma ray: electromagnetic wave.

Half-life

 OCR B   P 4f/g
EDEXCEL   P2.11

A radioactive source contains millions of nuclei. The number of nuclei decaying per unit time is called the **activity** of the source. The activity depends on two things:
● the type of isotope – some isotopes are more stable than others
● the number of undecayed nuclei in the sample – double the number of nuclei and, on average, there will be double the number of decays per second.

Over a period of time the activity of a source gradually dies away.

> **KEY POINT**
>
> The **half-life** of an isotope is the average time taken for half of the active nuclei to decay.

Technetium-99m (Tc-99m) decays by gamma emission to technetium-99 (Tc-99) with a half-life of six hours. After six hours, on average, only half of the Tc-99m nuclei remain active. After another six hours, on average, only one quarter of the nuclei are active. This is shown on the graph in Fig. 12.5. This pattern is the same for all isotopes but the value of the half-life is different. Carbon-14 has a half-life of 5730 years, but some isotopes have a half-life of less than a second.

Tc-99m is one of the most widely used radioactive isotopes in medicine. It is used to diagnose problems in many organs. The half-life of six hours means that the radiation lasts only long enough for the isotope to travel to the organ being investigated. Its activity decreases rapidly and cannot be detected after a few days. Tc-99m does not occur naturally – it is made in reactors.

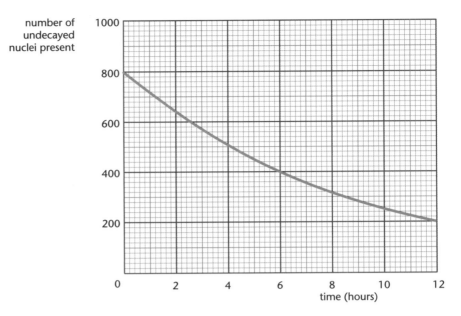

Fig. 12.5 The decay of a sample radioactive nuclei with a half-life of six hours.

Dating

The amount of carbon-14 in a living object is fixed when it dies. The carbon-14 decays, so that a wooden spear that is 5730 years old has only half the carbon-14 left that it had when it was made. Objects that once lived can be carbon dated by the amount of carbon-14 that is left.

Some rocks contain a radioactive isotope of uranium that decays to lead, so they can be dated by the uranium – lead ratio, the more lead there is the older the rock is.

Because of the small amounts of isotopes involved, and the long half-lifes, these methods cannot be used to find dates to within tens of years. They are not useful for objects that are less than a hundred years old.

12.4 *Nuclear reactors*

Nuclear fission

If a nucleus of uranium-235 absorbs a neutron, it becomes very unstable and can split into two nuclei of about equal size, and two or three neutrons. This process is called **nuclear fission**.

When this happens a lot of nuclear energy is released, about a **million times more** than the energy released in a chemical reaction.

The neutrons released can strike more uranium nuclei and cause more fission reactions – which in turn produce more neutrons, and so on. This is called a **chain reaction**.

If the fission reaction runs out of control it is an atomic bomb, but if the process is controlled, the energy released can be used to generate power. This is how a **nuclear reactor** in a **power station** works.

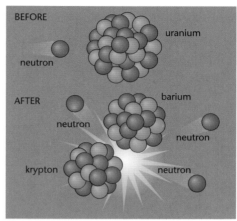

Fig. 12.6 A neutron absorbed by a uranium nucleus causes nuclear fission.

The **fuel rods** contain uranium-235 and are put in the reactor. The reaction can be controlled or stopped by using a material that absorbs neutrons. The neutron absorbing material is made into **control rods**. The control rods are moved into the reactor to absorb neutrons, and slow or stop the reaction, and out of the reactor to increase the reaction.

The energy heats up the fuel rods and control rods. A **coolant** is circulated to remove the heat from the reactor. When the coolant has been heated it is used to heat water to steam for the power station. When the coolant is cool it circulates through the reactor again.

This diagram shows how one neutron striking a U-235 nucleus can set off a chain reaction.

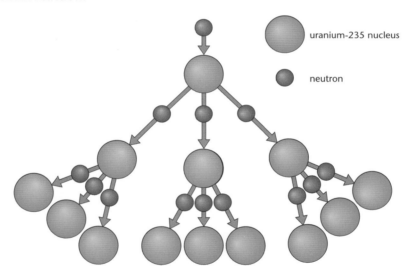

uranium-235 nucleus

neutron

Fig. 12.7 A chain reaction.

Waste disposal

Radioactive waste is dangerous to living things and must be carefully disposed of. The half-life of some isotopes is thousands, or millions, of years, so radioactive material must be disposed of in a way that will keep it safely contained for thousands of years.

There are three types of radioactive waste:
● **low-level waste** – for example, used protective clothing
● **intermediate-level waste** – for example, material from reactors
● **high-level waste** – for example, used fuel rods.

Low-level waste can be sealed into containers and put in landfill sites.

Intermediate-level waste is mixed with concrete and stored in stainless-steel containers. It must be stored for thousands of years.

High-level waste is kept in cooling tanks at first because it decays so fast it gets hot. Eventually it becomes intermediate-level waste. High-level waste includes 'weapons grade plutonium', which is the radioactive element plutonium, produced in nuclear reactors. It can be used to make nuclear weapons.

Waste can be dispersed (for example when sewage is discharged in the sea), or contained (for example when rubbish is put in a landfill site). Some radioactive waste is too dangerous to be dispersed.

Where to store the waste?

- At the bottom of the sea – but containers may leak.
- Underground – but containers may leak, and earthquakes or other changes to the rocks may occur.
- On the surface – but needs guarding (for example, from terrorists) for thousands of years.
- Blast into space – but danger of rocket explosion.

The precautionary principle says that if we are not sure of the effect of something, and it could be very harmful, then we should not risk trying it. (It is better to be safe than sorry.)

Nuclear fusion

The protons and neutrons inside the nucleus are held together by a force called the strong force. When two small nuclei are close enough together they can fuse together and form a larger nuclei. When they do this they release a large amount of energy. The problem is getting the two nuclei close enough for the strong force to take effect, because nuclei are positively charged and repel each other.

Inside stars the temperatures are high enough for the nuclei to have enough energy to get close enough for the strong force to take over and nuclear fusion occurs.

Scientific research is continuing to try and control the nuclear fusion reaction and produce nuclear fusion reactors.

HOW SCIENCE WORKS

OCR B   P4g

EDEXCEL 360   P2.11

Radioactivity benefits and risks

In the USA in the 1920s, you could buy 'The Curie RadioActive Re-Generator and Stone Water Filter' Fig. 12.8. It was made by the Curie Radium Company and was sold as 'A water jar in which is placed your local drinking water. In this jar is also placed a Radium Ore Disc - this disc throws off light rays thereby forming niton gas, making the water radioactive, the same as the Great Health Springs. Radioactive water is a proven means to health as millions can testify.'

Today we would say the radioactive disc is made of uranium ore and gives off radon gas.

Radium glows in the dark so, from about 1917, radium-containing paint was used to paint luminescent hands and numbers on watches. Many workers were young girls. They were encouraged to use their lips to make the tip of the brush into a point. Radium-226 was absorbed into their bones. One girl reported that after blowing her nose the handkerchief glowed in the dark. After 1923 the link between radium dial painting and health problems began to be noticed, and the practice of using lips to point the brush, was discontinued around 1926.

In the 1970s radiotherapy for breast cancer was not as advanced as it is today. The dose had to be high enough to kill the cancer cells, or the cancer would return. In 2006 a woman died as a result of the large dose of radiation she received during a 20 week course of radiotherapy in 1972. The high dose was standard practice at the time. This woman lived for another 34 years but women who did not have the treatment died within a few years, when the cancer returned.

HOW SCIENCE WORKS

Jack had cancer of the thyroid gland. This gland in the neck absorbs iodine. To treat the cancer cells doctors gave Jack a drink containing radioactive iodine-131. For a few days beforehand he had to avoid eating and drinking products containing iodine, so that the radioactive iodine would be absorbed by his body. After taking the treatment Jack stayed in a side-room in the hospital. The visitors and nurses did not stay in the room very long because he was radioactive. Children were not allowed to visit him, and the nurse checked the radioactivity level with a Geiger counter. His urine was radioactive, so he had to flush the toilet several times to dilute it. Before he left, the books he had been reading were checked with a Geiger counter. After a few days the level of radioactivity had dropped to the normal background level and Jack was allowed to go home. The next check-up showed that the cancer cells had been killed by the radioactive iodine.

thyroid gland

This table compares the risks of different activities by working out an average of days of life lost for each activity. This is worked out by:

$$\frac{\text{total days of life lost by all the people who died early}}{\text{total population}}$$

Activity	Average days/years lost
Smoking 20 cigarettes a day	6 years
All accidents	207 days
Cancer due to being exposed to 3 mSv of radiation (average normal background)	15 days
Cancer due to being exposed to 10 mSv of radiation	51 days

HOW SCIENCE WORKS *Questions*

1. Explain whether you think the benefit is worth the risk.
   (a) of using the The Curie RadioActive Re-Generator and Stone Water Filter
   (b) of using the lips to get a point on a brush of radium-containing paint
   (c) for the woman who had the 1970s breast cancer treatment
   (d) of treating thyroid cancer with radioactive iodine   [4]
2. Why is the The Curie RadioActive Re-Generator and Stone Water Filter not on sale today?   [2]
3. One of Jack's friends, who is a smoker, avoided him after Jack left hospital because he was afraid Jack might be radioactive. Jack said that his friend was more at risk from smoking.
   (a) Use the table above to explain why Jack was correct.
   (b) Suggest why Jack's friend was more worried about radioactivity than smoking.   [2]

Exam practice questions

1. $^{235}_{92}$U and $^{238}_{92}$U are both isotopes of uranium. Which of these tables is correct?

    A

isotope	protons	neutrons
$^{235}_{92}$U	92	235
$^{238}_{92}$U	92	238

    B

isotope	protons	neutrons
$^{235}_{92}$U	92	143
$^{238}_{92}$U	92	146

    C

isotope	protons	neutrons
$^{235}_{92}$U	235	92
$^{238}_{92}$U	238	92

    D

isotope	protons	neutrons
$^{235}_{92}$U	143	92
$^{238}_{92}$U	146	92

    [1]

2. The half-life of technetium-99m is 6 hours. At the start of treatment the activity of a source of technetium-99m is 8000 counts per minute. After 24 hours the activity is:
    A   333 counts per minute
    B   500 counts per minute
    C   1333 counts per minute
    D   4000 counts per minute   **[1]**

3. Factory waste is discharged from a pipe at sea. To check that it is not being washed up on a nearby beach, a radioactive tracer is added. A suitable isotope to use would be:
    A   an alpha emitter with a half-life of 1 year
    B   a beta emitter with a half-life of 2 days
    C   a beta emitter with a half-life of 1 year
    D   a gamma emitter with a half-life of 2 days   **[1]**

4. Put these statements in order to describe how the age of a wooden spear is determined using carbon dating. Start with **(c)**.
    A   A sample of the wood is tested to find the proportion of carbon-14
    B   The proportion of carbon-14 in the wood falls as the nuclei decay
    C   Carbon dioxide, containing some carbon-14, is taken in by the living tree during photosynthesis
    D   The tree is cut down and no more carbon –14 is taken in
    E   The result is compared with living wood and only half of the carbon-14 is left
    F   The wood is made into a spear
    G   The age of the spear is one half-life, which is 5730 years   **[3]**

5. **(a)**   Explain what is meant by **background radiation**.
    (b)   Write down one source of background radiation.   **[2]**

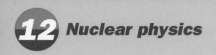

Exam practice questions

6. Write **T** for the **true** and **F** for the **false** statements below.
    (a) Nuclear reactors use fuel rods made of uranium –235 or plutonium-239.
    (b) The nucleus splits into two parts, this is called nuclear fusion.
    (c) A chain reaction occurs when a nucleus splits and releases a few neutrons which can be absorbed by other nuclei and cause them to split.
    (d) Control rods are lowered into the nuclear reactor core to speed up the reaction.
    (e) The energy released when the nuclei split heats up the reactor core. Coolant is circulated to remove the heat.
    (f) The removed fuel rods contain radioactive isotopes with very long half-lifes.   **[3]**

7. Use words from the list to complete the sentences below. (Use words once, more than once or not at all.)

alpha	**aluminium**	**beta**	**empty**	**gold**	**large**	**most**
negative	**none**	**positive**	**some**	**small**	**space**	

    Hans Geiger and Ernest Marsden fired _____**1**_____ particles at very thin _____**2**_____ foil. They counted the small flashes of light as the particles hit fluorescent screens and discovered that _____**3**_____ of the particles passed straight through the foil without being deflected. This showed that the atom was mostly _____**4**_____ _____**5**_____. A few of the particles were sent back towards the source. This showed that the atom had a _____**6**_____ nucleus with a _____**7**_____ charge.   **[7]**

8. Sodium–24 is a radioactive isotope of sodium that emits gamma radiation. The stable form of sodium is sodium–23.
    a) Explain how the nuclear structure of sodium-24 is different to sodium-23   **[1]**

    The activity of a sodium-24 source was measured over 2 days and this graph was plotted.

    (b) Use the graph to work out the half-life of sodium-24.   **[2]**
    (c) Use the graph to estimate the background activity at the site of the experiment.   **[1]**
    (d) Explain whether a salt of sodium-24 would be a suitable isotope to use for :
        i) the source in a smoke detector
        ii) a tracer to find the leak in an underground water pipe.   **[4]**

Rearranging formulae

If you are asked to write down a formula or equation, do not write down only the triangle – or you will get no marks.

The formulae that you need in the exam are written on the exam paper. OCR A and OCR B have a sheet labelled useful 'relationships' or 'formulae'. Edexcel 360 has each formula written in a box as part of the question.

You may need to rearrange a formula. Some students find using this triangle method useful.

Example 1 $speed = \frac{distance}{time}$

To calculate distance:

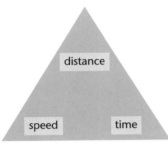

1. Write the formula into a triangle, so that distance is 'over' time. This means putting distance at the top, time can go in either of the other corners.
2. Cover the word distance with your finger and look at the position of speed and time. They are side by side, so distance = speed x time.
3. To find the time, cover time with your finger and distance is 'over' speed, so $time = \frac{distance}{speed}$

Example 2 momentum = mass x velocity

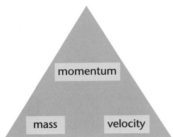

1. Write the formulae into a triangle so that mass and velocity are side by side. This means they must go in the two bottom corners of the triangle.
2. Covering mass gives $mass = \frac{momentum}{velocity}$
3. Covering velocity gives $velocity = \frac{momentum}{mass}$

List of formulae

	OCRA	OCRB	AQA	EDEXCEL
$speed = \frac{distance}{time}$	P4	P3		
$velocity = \frac{displacement}{time}$	P4			P2
$acceleration = \frac{change\ in\ velocity}{time\ taken\ for\ change}$		P3	P2	P2
weight = mass x gravitational field strength	P4		P2	
Resultant force = mass x acceleration		P3	P2	P2
Kinetic energy = $\frac{1}{2}$ mass x speed ^{2}	P4	P3	P2	P2
Change in gravitational potential energy = mass x gravitational field strength x height difference	P4	P3		P2
momentum = mass x velocity	P4		P2	P2
$force = \frac{change\ in\ momentum}{time\ taken\ for\ change}$	P4		P2	
potential difference = current x resistance OR $resistance = \frac{voltage}{current}$	P5	P4	P2	
$power = \frac{energy\ transformed}{time}$ OR $Power = \frac{work\ done}{time\ taken}$	P5	P3	P2	P2
Energy transferred (or transformed) = work done	P4		P2	P2
Work done = force x distance moved in direction of force	P4	P3	P2	P2
power = current x potential difference	P5		P2	
energy transferred (or transformed) = potential difference x charge			P2	
charge = current x time			P2	
Electrical energy = voltage x current x time	P5			P2
For a transformer the ratio of the voltages is the same as the ratio of turns in the coils; $\frac{V_p}{V_s} = \frac{N_p}{N_s}$	P5			
Efficiency = energy usefully transferred/total energy supplied x 100	P5			
Wave speed = frequency x wavelength	P6			

Answers

Chapter 1

How Science Works

'I think that it is wrong...' – person may be worried that cloned embryos are being destroyed to extract stem cells and may think that this is destroying (potential) human life.

'I am not happy...' – person may think that it is wrong to only allow this treatment to be available for people who can afford it.

'I think that more people... – An unfertilised egg cannot develop into a person so it is acceptable to destroy it to extract stem cells.

Exam practice questions

1. 1 **A** 2 **D** 3 **C** 4 **B**

2.

	Osmosis	Diffusion	Active transport
Can cause a substance to enter a cell	✓	✓	✓
Needs energy from respiration	✗	✗	✓
Can move a substance against a concentration gradient	✗	✗	✓
Is responsible for oxygen moving into the red blood cells in the lungs	✗	✓	✗

3.

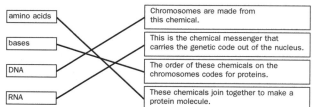

4.

The number of chromosomes in a human body cell.	46
The number of cells made from one cell when it divides by meiosis.	4
The number of chromosomes in a human sperm cell.	23
The number of strands in each DNA molecule.	2

5. **(a)** On the chromosomes in the nucleus
 (b) Each gene has a different order of bases.
 The bases code for the order of amino acids in the protein.
 (c) 1094/20 000 x 100 = 5.47%
 (d) The liver
 Uses the most genes and they code for different enzymes

6. **(a)** Lives underwater
 Makes bubbles of oxygen that can be counted
 (b) oxygen
 (c) **(i)** He uses the same piece of pondweed throughout
   (ii) He counts the bubbles three times at each light intensity
 (d) Use a more accurate timer

Chapter 2

How Science Works

1. More likely to convince people because they believe it is based on scientific fact.

2. The first article tends to concentrate on the environmental effects of farming. It does not consider the health issues.

3. They have different backgrounds such as different jobs. They have picked up different views from their parents. Some may have strong views on animal rights.

Exam practice questions

1. 1 **B** 2 **D** 3 **C** 4 **A**

2.

Spreading manure on the fields	
Spraying chemical pesticides	✓
Killing weeds using weedkillers	✓
Rotating their crops	

3.

nitrogen fixing bacteria — break down organic remains

decomposing bacteria — convert ammonium compounds to nitrates

nitrifying bacteria — convert nitrate to nitrogen gas

denitrifying bacteria — convert nitrogen gas to nitrogen compounds

4. **(a)** 10%
 (b) heat / excretion / uneaten parts / egestion
 (c) 200 kJ
 (d) So much energy is lost at each stage, there is not enough energy left to support another level
 (e) Leaves are broken down by decomposers
 They give off carbon dioxide, in respiration
 The carbon dioxide is used by the trees for photosynthesis

5. **(a)**

Sales of organic foods are increasing dramatically	F
Organic food is better for people	C
Much organic food is dearer than intensively produced food	F
Organic food tastes better than non-organic food	C
Artificial additives can make food look more colourful.	F

 (b) People are worried about the effect on the environment of growing non-organically
 They do not want to take the risk that the non-organic food may be harmful
 (c) Some countries are struggling to produce enough food   Growing organically may reduce yields / cause starvation

Chapter 3

How Science Works

1. **(a)** Far more people require a transplant than are receiving them.
 (b) The number of people requiring transplants is increasing.
 The gap between the number of people requiring a transplant and the number that are receiving them is getting wider.

2. (a–b) The answer depends on a person's ethical views but arguments include ideas about personal choice and also should people be allowed to gain even if they are not prepared to donate.
 (c) Possible factors include: the age of the patient, how ill they are, how likely they are to survive, if the damage is self inflicted.

Exam practice questions

1. 1 **D** 2 **B** 3 **C** 4 **A**

2.

Their muscles will contract uncontrollably	
The blood vessels in the skin widen	✓
The sweat gland become less active	
The pituitary gland releases less ADH	

3.

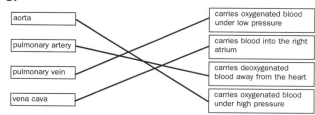

4. **(a)** digested by amylase enzymes, in the mouth and small intestine, maltose then digested by maltase
   (b) (i) ten minutes
   (ii) Starch needs to de digested
   Glucose needs to be absorbed
   (c) (i) 280 μg per 100 cm³
   (ii) blood glucose levels rise, detected by the pancreas, insulin released to bring blood glucose levels down
   (d) Insulin levels would not rise so high, Glucose levels would rise higher / stay higher for longer
5. **(a)** organs are too complicated / difficulty in powering them / may be rejected
   (b)

Some peoples organs could be removed in error	
It would increase the number of organs available for transplants	✓
It would avoid having to ask relatives about donation	✓
Some people have religious objections to transplants	

   (c) Forget to do anything about it, say they are willing but really they do not wish to donate

Chapter 4

How Science Works

(a) There is no indication that other factors in the women were taken into account or kept constant.
(b) Asking the women about their eating habits would not give a precise record of their vitamin A intake.

Exam practice questions

1. 1 **C** 2 **A** 3 **B** 4 **D**
2. **(a)** D, A, B, C
   (b)

the process uses hormones to cut DNA	✗
the Bacteria can be grown in large fermenters	
the insulin produced is a hybrid of human and bacterial insulin	✗
the bacteria can be grown on cheap waste products	

3. **(a)**

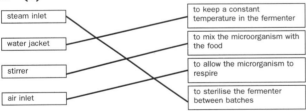

   (b) (i) dung / farmyard waste
   (ii) does not cause so much pollution, sustainable / will not run out, does not have to be transported around
4. **(a) (i)** B
   (ii) A
   (b) No, the method does not take into account how serious each defect is
   (c) This is because they have different views on whether it is correct to use genetic engineering They are trying to back up their argument

Chapter 5

How Science Works

1. D
2.
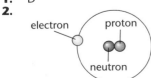

3. Hydrogen has a similar arrangement of electrons to the Group 1 metals (1 electron in the outer shell)
4. The ions of lithium and sodium 'float' in a sea of electrons. The electrons move when a potential different is applied.
5.

   p is a proton

   e– is an electron

   Mercury melts at −39°C and boils at 359°C.
6. **(a)** liquid
   (b) solid
7. It has a different physical property – hydrogen is a colourless gas.
8. According to the definition given the answer is 'no'. The magnetic radiation is not coming from a biological agent or condition.

Exam practice questions

1. C
2. D
3. C
4.

1	protons	**2**	neutrons
3	electrons	**4**	shells
5	nucleus	**6**	electrons
7	protons	**8**	electrons
9	neutrons	**10**	isotopes

5.

Compound	Type of element	bonding
sodium chloride (NaCl)	sodium metal / chlorine non-metal	ionic
ammonia (NH₃)	nitrogen non-metal / hydrogen non-metal	covalent
methane (CH₄)	carbon non-metal / hydrogen non-metal	covalent
calcium oxide	calcium metal / oxygen non-metal	ionic
magnesium phosphide	magnesium metal / phosphorus non-metal	ionic

6. atoms only → helium
   giant ionic compound → magnesium oxide
   giant molecular structure → silicon dioxide
   giant structure of atoms → graphite
   metallic structure → copper
   nanomolecule → Buckminster fullerene
   simple molecular structure → sulfur
7. **(a)**   **(b)**

8. **(a)** False. Ozone is very pale blue and oxygen is colourless.
   (b) False. The oxygen atoms in both molecules contain 8 protons and 8 neutrons.
   (c) True. The relative molecular mass of ozone is 48 and the relative molecular mass of oxygen is 32. Density of ozone will be $\frac{48}{24} = 2.0\,g/dm^3$ and oxygen will be $\frac{32}{24} = 1.33\,g/dm^3$ (1 mole of any gas occupies 24 dm³)
   (d) True. Oxygen has two atoms of oxygen and ozone has three atoms of oxygen. The number of electrons in an atom is equal to the number of protons.

Answers

9. **(a)** **(i)** 14 Silicon comes between aluminium (atomic number 130 and phosphorus (atomic number 15), hence it will have a value of 14.
   (ii) 28 The atomic mass is double the atomic number for most of the first 20 elements.
   (b) **(i)** Element X is Ar (argon), element Y is K (potassium)
   (ii) Element S is Ar (argon) element T is Ca (calcium)
   (c) Mass number is the number of protons and neutrons, both of which have a mass of 1 unit.
   (d) **(i)** 9 parts Ne-20 and 1 part Ne-22.
   (ii) Cl (chlorine)

Chapter 6
How Science Works

1. D
2. **(a)** isomers
   (b) vinyl alcohol   ethanal

   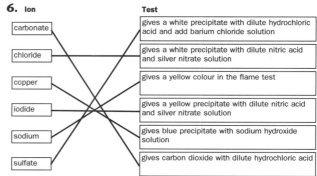

   (c) Vinyl alcohol rapidly changes into ethanal.
   In *addition polymerisation* the polymer contains the same monomer joined together many times to form a polymer. The polymer has the same empirical formula as the monomer.
3. **(a)**

   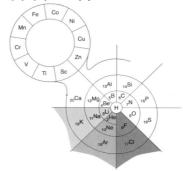

   ethene   repeating unit of poly(ethene)

   (b) C_2H_4O
4. Arguments such as
   Washing clothes uses detergent which can pollute water and detergents are expensive.
   Cotton is a renewable fabric.
   Clothes made of cotton take time to decompose.
   PVOH clothing is easy to dispose of.
   PVOH uses a non-renewable source.

Exam practice questions

1. A
2. C
3. B
4. The alkanes are hydrocarbons. This means they contain carbon and *hydrogen*. only. The start of each name tells us how many *carbon* atoms there are in one *molecule*. Meth means *one* and prop means *three*.
   The alkanes can be represented by the *general* formula C_nH_{2n+2}. When n = 4 the alkane is *butane*
   As the relative molecular mass of the alkanes increases the *boiling* point of the alkanes also increases.
   All alkanes burn in an excess of oxygen to form *carbon dioxide* and water.
   Alkanes are mainly used as *fuels*
5.

Halogen	Symbol	State at r.t.p.	Formula of compound with sodium	Electronic configuration
fluorine	F	gas	pale yellow	2.7
chlorine	Cl	gas	green	2.8.7
bromine	Br	liquid	orange/brown	2 8 18 7
iodine	I	solid	black	2 8 18 18 7

6.

Ion	Test
carbonate	gives a white precipitate with dilute hydrochloric acid and add barium chloride solution
chloride	gives a white precipitate with dilute nitric acid and silver nitrate solution
copper	gives a yellow colour in the flame test
iodide	gives a yellow precipitate with dilute nitric acid and silver nitrate solution
sodium	gives blue precipitate with sodium hydroxide solution
sulfate	gives carbon dioxide with dilute hydrochloric acid

7. **(a)** **(b)** and **(c)**.

8. **(a)** **(i)** **C**
   (i) **B** Addition of an alkaline substance such as calcium oxide
   (ii) **A** Highest potassium and nitrate content. Potassium nitrate is a fertiliser.
   (b) any two from $Ca(NO_3)_2$; KNO_3; $CaSO_4$; K_2SO_4
   (c) **(i)** bilberry or cranberry
   (ii) sugar beet
   (iii) peas
9. **(a)** Add anhydrous copper(II) sulfate, it changes from white to blue if water is present.
   (b) **(i)** A protein that acts as a catalyst
   (ii) A chemical reaction of a compound with water
   The hydrolysis of lactose produces glucose ($C_6H_{12}O_6$) and galactose (($C_6H_{12}O_6$))
   (iii) Isomers
   (iv) $C_{12}H_{22}O_{11} + H_2O \rightarrow + C_6H_{12}O_6 + C_6H_{12}O_6$
   (v) COOH
   $\mid$ Most of the protein in milk is in the
   HCOH form of casein.
   $\mid$
   CH$_3$
   (c) amino acids
   Milk is an emulsion containing unsaturated fats.
   (d) **(i)** A suspension of small drops of one liquid in another liquid with which the first will not mix.
   (ii) Add bromine water. It will change colour from orange/brown to colourless if a compound is unsaturated.
   (e) Calcium

Chapter 7
How Science Works

1. **(a)** methane
   (b) $CH_4 + H_2O \rightarrow 3H_2 + CO$
2. $N_2(g) + 3H_2(g) \rightarrow 2NH_3(g)$
3. The thermoplastic would melt at the temperature of the reaction.
4. **(a)** reduced – it has gained electrons
   (b) It would have no effect – there are the same number of gaseous molecules on each side of the equilibrium reaction

5. **(a)** 40%
   (b) It is the highest temperature that can be produced by the nuclear power station.
6. Heat energy produced from chemical energy.
7. uses a renewable source (water)
   reagents are recycled
   no effluent
8. leaks of radioactive substances
   hot concentrated sulfuric acid is highly corrosive

Exam practice questions

1. D
2. B
3. B
4. For particles to react they must *collide* with each other.
   Only particles with a certain amount of energy called the *activation* energy react.
   If the *size* of the reacting particles is decreased, there is more *surface* area available for reacting and the speed of the reaction *increases*
   When a solution becomes more *concentrated* the number of particles present increases.
   Increasing the *temperature* increases the rate of the reaction.
   One of the ways a *catalyst* is thought to work is by lowering the *energy* required before the reaction takes place. It speeds up the reaction but is *unchanged* at the end of the reaction.

5.

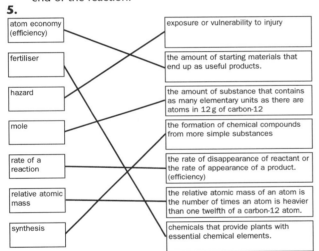

6. **(a)** Use either the word **fast** or **slow** describe the rate of the following reactions:
      (i) fast   **(ii)** fast   **(iii)** slow
   (b) oxygen, manganese(IV) oxide
7. **(a)** temperature graph – the rate increases until the temperature reaches about 37°C (body temperature) – the enzyme is then destroyed as the temperature increases beyond this point (denatured)
      pH graph – the rate increases until a pH of about 7.3 is reached. Increase in the pH (alkalinity) destroys the enzyme (denatured)
   (b) temperature of 37°C and pH 7.2
8. **(a)** **(i)** chlorine is poisonous gas.
      (ii) U-tube got warm; change of colour
      (ii) write the equation for the formation of iodine monochloride. I2(s) + Cl(g) → ICl(l)
   (b) **(i)** chlorine is denser than air
         the reaction is reversible
      (ii) ICl(l) + Cl2(g) → ICl3(s)
9. **(a)** **(i)** to remove solid particles from air
      (ii) larger surface area for reactants to meet thus speeding up the reaction.
      (iii) because oxygen is required in the first two reactions
      (iv) to conserve energy
   (b) **(i)** ammonia and air (oxygen)
      (ii) = 77.8%

(c) ammonia is an irritant
   nitric acid is a powerful oxidising agent
   reaction is very exothermic
(d) 22.68 kg
(e) Continuous process. The nitric acid is continually drawn off as the ammonia and oxygen are fed in to reacting vessels.
   (The only time the process is stopped is to change the catalyst. and for maintenance.)

Chapter 8
How Science Works

DCPIP titration
1. keep the titration away from too much heat and light
   perform the titration as rapidly as possible
   make sure that no other reducing agents can get into the titration apparatus
2. 9.4 cm³ Since this is the least amount of DCPIP required – some of the ascorbic acid must have been reduced, thus requiring less DCPIP
3. Average titre is = 9.6cm3 (ignoring highest and lowest values)
   Mass of vitamin C in 5 cm³ = 9.6 x 0.1 = 0.96 mg
   Mass in 100 cm³ of solution = 0.96 x 20 = 19.2 mg
   This is also the mass in 25 g of Brussels sprout
   Mass in 100 g = 19.2 x 4 = 76.8 mg
Iodine titration
4. Average titre is 27.3 cm³
   Mass of vitamin C = 27.3 x 8.81 = 240
   Therefore the tablets must be 250 mg tablets (240 is the nearest value to 250)
5. volume of iodine solution required would be very small thus making the titration less accurate
Vitamin C
6. **(a)** $C_6H_8O_6$ **(b)** $C_3H_4O_3$
7. **(a)** reduces   **(b)** reduces
   (c) slight loss   **(d)** reduces
8. **(a)** no – it does not contain a –COOH group
   (b) no – it is not produced naturally in the human body.

Exam practice questions

1. B
2. C
3. D
4. All salts are *ionic* compounds. A salt is formed when a *metal* ion or an ammonium ions replaces one or more *hydrogen* ions of an *acid*.
   Salts that contain water of crystallisation are called *hydrated* salts. Salts that **DO NOT** contain water of crystallisation are called *anhydrous* salts.
   Zinc sulfate can be made by reacting zinc carbonate with *sulfuric* acid. The gas given off is *carbon dioxide*. Also formed in this reaction is *water*.
   All *sodium* salts are soluble in water. Insoluble salts are usually prepared by *precipitation*.
5.

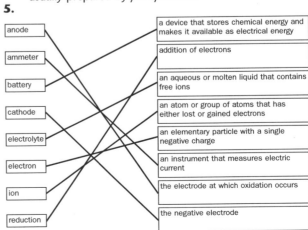

6. **(a) (i)** and **(ii)**
   (b) (i) pH 4 **(ii)** time 45 minutes
   (c) (i) acid **(ii)** using a pH meter
7. **Group 1** Not true. Some organic substances such as ethanol react with sodium to form hydrogen.
   Group 2 Not true. Some substances including alkalis have a bitter taste which are not acids. It is a dangerous test.
   Group 3 Yes this is true. An acid such as nitric acid donates its electron to a base such as copper(II) oxide to form a salt and water
   Group 4 Yes, this is true. Acids contain H^+ ions and when added to water they increase the concentration of H^+ ions
   Group 5 Not true. Hydrochloric acid (HCl) is an acid but it does not contain oxygen.
   Group 6 Not true. Organic compounds contain hydrogen, most of these are not acids. All ammonia contains hydrogen. Ammonia dissolves in water to form an alkaline solution.
8.

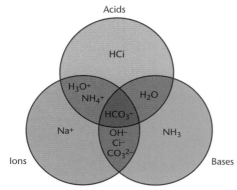

9. **(a)** chlorine
   (b) chlorine is slightly soluble in water
   (c) iron reacts with chlorine
   (d) H^+; SO_4^{2-}; OH^-
   (e) (i) oxygen
      (ii) hydrogen
   (f) $4OH^- - 4e^- \rightarrow 2H_2O + O_2$ $2H^+ + 2e^- \rightarrow H_2$
   (g) $80\,cm^3$
   (h) oxygen would be formed at the anode
      $4OH^-(aq) - 4e^- \rightarrow 2H_2O(l) + O_2(g)$
      oxygen would react with carbon electrode to form carbon dioxide $C(s) + O_2(g) \rightarrow CO_2(g)$
      carbon dioxide would react with calcium hydroxide to give white precipitate of calcium carbonate
      $Ca(OH)_2(aq) + CO_2(g) \rightarrow CaCO_3(s) + H_2O(l)$

Chapter 9
How Science Works

1. mass/the rate that time passes
2. B
3. Because the time shifts measured were all less than 300nm; so the results would not have been significant/would have been within the range of the measurements
4. It took this long to develop a stable and accurate enough clock.

Exam practice questions

1. **(a) (i)** D
      (ii) C
   (b) D
   (c) C
2. 1 pair, 2* equal, 3* opposite, 4* action, 5* reaction, 6 foot, 7 backward, 8 ground, 9 ground 10 forward, 11 foot, 12 friction, *2 and 3 can be reversed, 4 and 5 can be reversed
3. (D) B C E A F

4. lines joining A2 B1 C4 D3
5. **(a)** 800 x 10 x 80 = 640 000J
   (b) gain in KE = loss in PE = 640 000J
   (c) $640\,000 = \frac{1}{2}\,mv^2 = \frac{1}{2}\,x\,80\,v^2$,
      v = ÷ 1600 m/s = 40 m/s
   (d) 25 000 ÷ 10 = 2 500 N
6. **(a)** steady speed, resultant = 0, so driving force = 5000 N
   (b) $\frac{1}{2}$ x 3000 x (30)^{2}J = 1 575 000 N
   (c) momentum= 3000 x 30 = –105 000 kg m/s
      OR acceleration = (0–30) ÷ 5 = -6 m/s^2 (- for deceleration)
   (d) change in momentum ÷ time = 105 000 ÷ 5 = 21 000 N
      OR mass x acceleration = 3000 x 6 = 21 000 N
7. **(a)** 36
   (b) (i) drinking, tiredness etc (see page 156)
      (ii) icy road, poor tyres etc (see page 156)
   (c) $\frac{1}{2}$ x 60 x (20)^2 = 30 x 400 = 12 000 J
   (d) seatbelt stretches
   (e) reduces the stopping force on the body
   (f) The person feels safer, that the risk is less, so it is OK to drive faster
   (g) Road travel
   (h) Because she travels by road everyday this is a risk she is used to, but travelling by rail is an unfamiliar risk and people over-estimate unfamiliar risks

Chapter 10
How Science Works

1. C
2. 2.0 V
3. 2.5 V
4. **(a)** 0.9 mA
   (b) 17.8 mA

Exam practice questions

1. B
2. D
3. B
4.

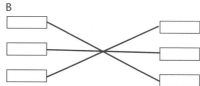

5. B E D C A
6. 1. chest 2. electrical 3. contract 4. charge 5. shock
7. **(a)** the case is a non-conductor
   (b) (i) current flows normally
      (ii) fuse melts and breaks circuit
   (c) will not melt until 13A flows, much higher current than needed
8. **(a)** the droplets will be charged and repel each other
   (b) droplets will be attracted to car body
   (c) even coverage all over – in shadows etc; less waste paint
9. **(a)** X is the ammeter Y is the voltmeter
   (b) 1050 mV
   (c) (i) brighter
      (ii) off
      (iii) dimmer
   (d) An a.c. power supply produces a current that keeps changing direction; d.c. is always in the same direction.
   (e) The current will only flow in the circuit when the voltage is in the forward direction. When the voltage is in the reverse direction the current will be zero, so the divide will flash on and off 50 times a second (so fast you can't tell).

Chapter 11
How Science Works

1. ADFBHGCE
2. Isaac Newton said light was not a wave and scientists thought he was such a great scientist he must be right no
3. no, because light shows wave behaviour; diffraction/interference/an example described such as Young's experiment

Answers to questions

1. B
2. A
3. D
4. false, true, true, true
5. modulate, carrier, transmitter, aerial, signal, demodulated
6.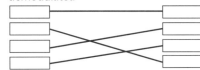

7. **(a)** sound with frequency higher than the upper threshold of human hearing
   (b) Some is reflected from each boundary between tissue layers. The reflections are used to build up an image
   (c) breaking up stones e.g. kidney stones
8. **(a)** A = compression B = rarefaction
   C = wavelength D = longitudinal
   (b) particles move up and down but they do not move along

Chapter 12
How Science Works

1. **(a)** No because radon is an alpha emitter and drinking it would expose you to a risk of cancer. There is no health benefit.
   (b) No, because there are safer ways to get a point to a brush, and the radium was a health risk.
   (c) Yes because she would have died many years earlier from cancer if she had not been treated
   (d) Yes because the cancer can be slowed or cured by the radioactive treatment, prolonging or improving the quality of life
2. There are risks to health and no benefits and it would contaminate people's homes
3. **(a)** The risk from being exposed to normal background amounts to 15 days lost on average, whereas the risk from smoking amounts to 6 years lost on average, so smoking is much more dangerous.
   (b) people are more worried about unfamiliar things and overestimate the risk.

Exam practice questions

1. B
2. B
3. B
4. C D F B A E G
5. **(a)** background radiation is the level of radioactive emissions that is all around us all the time.
   (b) one of, for example: cosmic rays, the Sun, rocks, leaks from radioactive waste.
6. **(a)** T **(b)** F **(c)** T **(d)** F **(e)** T **(f)** T
7. alpha, gold, most, empty, space, small, positive
8. **(a)** sodium-24 has one extra neutron
   (b) 15 hours
   (c) 20 counts per minute
   (d) (i) no because it would decay too fast and there would be no radioactivity left after a few weeks/because it is a gamma emitter and people who came close to it would be irradiated
   (ii) Yes because it is a gamma emitter; so the radiation from the pipe would reach the surface/because it has a short enough half-life not to contaminate the site for a long time

Index